Science 5
Learning Coach Guide

Part 2

At Stride, Inc. (NYSE: LRN) – formerly K12 Inc. – we are reimagining lifelong learning as a rich, deeply personal experience that prepares learners for tomorrow. Since its inception, Stride has been committed to removing barriers that impact academic equity and to providing high-quality education for anyone—particularly those in underserved communities. The company has transformed the teaching and learning experience for millions of people by providing innovative, high-quality, tech-enabled education solutions, curriculum, and programs directly to students, schools, the military, and enterprises in primary, secondary, and post-secondary settings. Stride is a premier provider of K–12 education for students, schools, and districts, including career learning services through middle and high school curriculum. Providing a solution to the widening skills gap in the workplace and student loan crisis, Stride equips students with real world skills for in-demand jobs with career learning. For adult learners, Stride delivers professional skills training in healthcare and technology, as well as staffing and talent development for Fortune 500 companies. Stride has delivered millions of courses over the past decade and serves learners in all 50 states and more than 100 countries. The company is a proud sponsor of the Future of School, a nonprofit organization dedicated to closing the gap between the pace of technology and the pace of change in education. More information can be found at stridelearning.com, K12.com, destinationsacademy.com, galvanize.com, techelevator.com, and medcerts.com.

978-1-60153-343-2

Printed by Bradford & Bigelow, Newburyport, MA, USA, May 2021.

Table of Contents

Learning Coach Guide
Lesson 1: Atoms and Elements

Everything, from a toothbrush to a mud puddle is made from atoms of elements. There are just over 100 identified elements known to the world today, but those elements make millions of compounds. Your student will learn to read chemical formulas and chemical equations and will investigate how properties change when compounds are formed from a chemical reaction.

All objects, from your next-door neighbor to the cardboard container holding your milk, are made of atoms. Although atoms are too small to be seen, they can be studied based on the way they react. Learn the basic structure of atoms and explore the arrangement of their subatomic particles.

Lesson Objectives

- Identify the three main parts of atoms as protons, electrons, and neutrons, and that protons have a positive charge, electrons a negative charge, and neutrons have no charge at all.
- Recognize that atoms of each element are exactly alike.
- State that atoms of different elements have different masses depending on the number of protons, electrons, and neutrons, but that most of the mass comes from the protons and neutrons.
- Describe the current model of the atom as a positively charged nucleus containing the protons and neutrons surrounded by electrons moving in certain regions within an electron "cloud."
- Describe the current model of the atom as a positively charged nucleus containing the protons and neutrons surrounded by electrons moving in certain regions within an "electron cloud".

PREPARE

Approximate lesson time is 60 minutes.

Materials

For the Student

    💻 At the Electron Hotel

For the Adult

    💻 At the Electron Hotel Answer Key

Lesson Notes

All matter, whether it is a solid, liquid, or gas, is made up of tiny particles called *atoms*. We can call atoms the "building blocks" of all matter. But individual atoms also have a shape and structure. Atoms are made up of tiny subatomic particles. There are three main kinds of subatomic particles: protons, electrons, and neutrons. Two have an electrical charge. Protons have a positive electrical charge, and electrons have a negative charge. Neutrons have no charge at all.

Protons and neutrons make up the center of the atom, called the *nucleus*. Electrons lie outside the nucleus. The atoms in different substances have different numbers of protons, neutrons, and electrons. A few substances are made up of only one type of atom. These substances are called *elements*.

The number of neutrons may vary from atom to atom, but a single atom has the same number of protons and electrons. An aluminum atom, for example, has 13 protons, 13 electrons, and 14 neutrons. An iron atom has 26 protons, 26 electrons, and 30 neutrons. Atoms also have mass. If you add up the number of protons and neutrons in the atoms of every kind element, you get the *atomic mass* of that element. An iron atom, for example, has 26 protons and 30 neutrons. So iron has an atomic mass of 56 (26 + 30 = 56). (Electrons are so small and have so little mass that they don't affect atomic mass.) But since the number of neutrons can vary from atom to atom, we can only estimate the atomic mass of an element.

Historic Atomic Models

For centuries scientists did not know that atoms existed. In the early 1800s, English chemist John Dalton came up with the theory that all matter is made of atoms. Dalton's atomic model showed the atom as a solid sphere. Nearly a hundred years later, English physicist J.J. Thomson discovered the electron. Thomson proved that atoms were not solid spheres. He showed that atoms were collections of smaller, subatomic particles. Thomson's atomic model showed an atom whose negatively charged electrons were stuck to a positively charged center. Following in Dalton and Thomson's footsteps, other scientists began to envision different models of atoms. Each model improved upon the earlier models.

In 1911, physicist Ernest Rutherford found that an atom's protons seemed to be clustered in the center of the atom with the electrons surrounding them. He called this center the *nucleus*. Rutherford's atomic model was an improvement over Thomson's. However, it did not explain why the negatively charged electrons stayed separate from the positively charged protons. In 1913, one of Rutherford's students, Neils Bohr, suggested that electrons orbit the nucleus like planets orbiting the sun. Bohr's idea was that electrons move within specific energy levels that surround the nucleus. The electrons in each level have a similar energy.

Electron Cloud Atomic Model

In the 1920s, Austrian physicist Erwin Schrödinger created the atomic model we use today. Schrödinger's version is called the *electron cloud* model. The main difference between Bohr's model and Schrödinger's is the path of the electrons around the nucleus. Instead of traveling in a certain path around the nucleus like planets orbiting the sun, the electrons in Schrödinger's model dart around within their own energy level. The position of electrons in Schrödinger's model is represented by an electron "cloud." The areas that electrons move through do not always take the shape of a sphere. Some take the shape of a dumbbell or even a cloverleaf.

Keywords and Pronunciation

atom : A tiny particle that is the fundamental building block of any substance. The properties of the atom determine the properties of the element made up of only those atoms.

electron : A tiny part of an atom with a negative electric charge. In an atom, electrons form a cloud around the nucleus.

Erwin Schrödinger (EHR-veen SHROH-ding-ur)

neutron : A particle in the nucleus of an atom, which has no electric charge. Atoms contain neutrons, electrons, and protons.

nucleus (NOO-klee-uhs) : The core of an atom made up of protons and neutrons. Electrons form a cloud around the nucleus of an atom.

proton : A tiny part of the nucleus of an atom, which has a positive electric charge. The number of protons determines the chemical properties of the atom.

subatomic : Particles that make up atoms. Protons, electrons, and neutrons are subatomic particles.

TEACH
Activity 1: Element-ary Science *(Online)*
Instructions

Have your student read through the Explore on his own. Reinforce and explain difficult concepts as needed.

Explore Suggestions:

Check your student's understanding by asking the following questions:

1. Name the parts of an atom and their charges. (proton: positive, electron: negative, neutron: neutral or no charge)
2. Think about how many times the model of an atom changed. Is it possible that it will change again? Why? (Yes, it is possible. But the current models are backed up by a vast amount of experimental data and are not likely to change in radical ways.)
3. Where is most of an atom's mass: in the protons and neutrons in the nucleus or in the electrons surrounding it? (in the protons and neutrons in the nucleus)

Screen 1: There are even smaller particles inside atoms called *quarks.* Visit Chem4Kids http://www.chem4kids.com/files/atom_intro.html for information about these super-tiny atomic particles.

Screen 6: Explain that atoms are too small to see. Scientists know about them because they do tests and can see how atoms behave.

After this activity, check to see if your student can:

- Recognize that atoms of each element are exactly alike; however, they may differ in the number of neutrons they have.
- Identify the three main parts of atoms as protons, electrons, and neutrons, and that protons have a positive charge, electrons a negative charge, and neutrons have no charge at all.
- Describe the electron cloud model of the atom as a positively charged nucleus containing the protons and neutrons surrounded by electrons moving in certain regions within an electron cloud.
- State that atoms of different elements have different masses depending on the number of protons, electrons, and neutrons, but that most of the mass comes from the protons and neutrons.

If your student has difficulty with any of these concepts, you may wish to review the Explore with him and have him explain the key points on each screen.

Activity 2: At The Electron Hotel *(Offline)*
Instructions

Teaching:

Protons, electrons, and neutrons are the three types of particles in an atom. Protons and neutrons are in the nucleus, with the electrons surrounding the nucleus in energy levels called *shells.* The number of protons and electrons are always the same in an electrically neutral atom.

The arrangement of electrons into shells follows special rules. Each energy level can hold a certain amount of electrons. The closer an electron is to the nucleus, the less energy it has--it cannot resist the attraction of the nucleus. Electrons can also jump between energy levels. A jump inward releases energy. A jump outward requires more energy.

What to Expect:

Your student should understand that electrons surround the nucleus in energy levels, moving in what looks like a cloud. The current model of the atom is called the *Electron Cloud* model.

Answers:
See answer key.

ASSESS
Lesson Assessment: Atoms and Elements (*Online*)

Students will complete an offline assessment based on the lesson objectives. Print the assessment and have students complete it on their own. Use the answer key to score the assessment, and then enter the results online. The attached answer key is the most current and may not coincide with previously printed guides.

<u>Name</u>   <u>Date</u>

At the Electron Hotel Answer Key

An atom's electrons are arranged in energy levels called *shells*. Which shell an electron is in depends on how much energy it has. Exactly how are these electrons arranged? Let's pay a visit to The Electron Hotel to find out.

The Electron Hotel is a happening place for atoms. It's an especially cool place to stay because there is plenty of room for electrons. Like any hotel, though, there are rules—in particular, at The Electron Hotel there are certain rules for where protons, electrons, and neutrons can be.

Imagine you work at the reception desk at The Electron Hotel. You have been given the following rules for atoms and data for floors. Study them carefully.

Electron Hotel Rules

Rule 1: Protons and neutrons must stay in the lobby (nucleus) at all times.

Rule 2: Electrons must stay in the floors above the lobby. (nucleus)

Rule 3: Each floor can hold only a certain number of electrons.

Rule 4: One floor must be full before you place electrons on the next highest floor.

1st floor	holds	2 electrons
2nd floor	holds	8 electrons
3rd floor	holds	18 electrons
4th floor	holds	32 electrons

At the Electron Hotel Answer Key

On a cold day, in walks an atom of sodium (symbol = Na). Sodium needs a place to stay. Sodium has 11 electrons. The picture below shows the floors sodium would fill at The Electron Hotel. Notice that the third floor isn't full. That's okay. Count the electrons to make sure there are 11. Then, try placing fluorine (symbol = F) into the hotel.

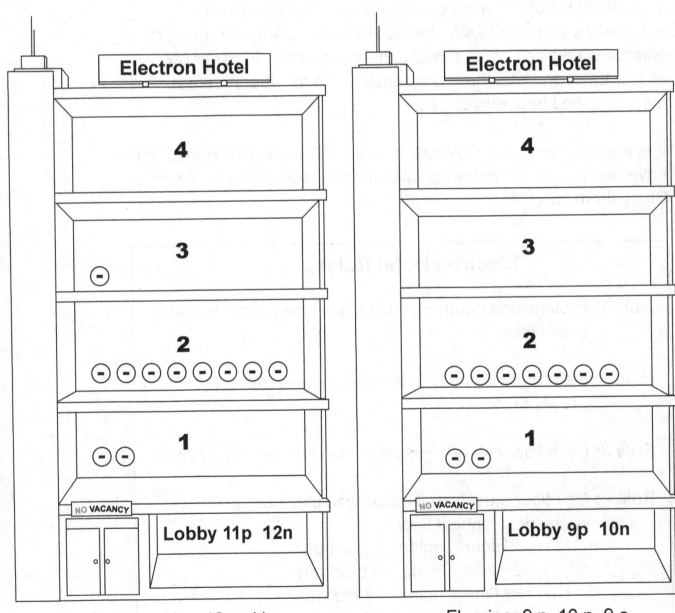

Sodium: 11 p, 12 n, 11 e   Fluorine: 9 p, 10 n, 9 e

At the Electron Hotel Answer Key

You know that, in real atoms, electrons are not arranged on floors. In the current model of atoms, the lobby is the atom's nucleus and the floors are really energy levels. Electrons move around the nucleus in energy levels, creating an electron cloud. Here's another way to show how electrons move around a nucleus. Study it, then sketch electrons in their energy levels for the following atoms. Stick to the rules of The Electron Hotel!

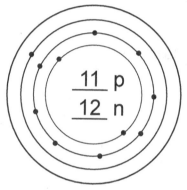

Sodium 11p, 12n, 11e

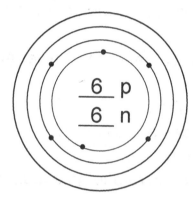

Carbon 6p, 6n, 6e

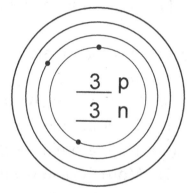

Lithium 3p, 3n, 3e

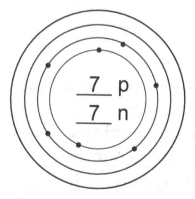

Nitrogen 7p, 7n, 7e

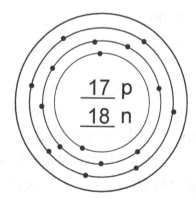

Chlorine 17p, 18n, 17e

Name _____ Date _____

Lesson Assessment Answer Key

Circle the correct answers and fill in the blanks.

1. What is the difference between two atoms of carbon having the same number of neutrons?
   Ⓐ Nothing.
   B. The number of protons.
   C. The number of electrons.
   D. There may be differences in how they react with oxygen.

2. What is the difference between an atom of silver and an atom of gold?
   A. One is new and the other is old.
   B. Their net electrical charges are different.
   Ⓒ Their atomic masses are different.
   D. More people would rather have one gold atom than a lot of gold.

3. List the three main parts of an atom and their electrical charges.
   proton: positive
   electron: negative
   neutron: neutral or no charge

4. Describe what the electron cloud model of the atom looks like. Explain where most of an atom's mass comes from. _____
   The electron cloud model has protons and neutrons
   in the nucleus and electrons surrounding the nucleus
   in energy levels that are not necessarily spherical, but
   shaped in an electron cloud. Most of an atom's mass
   comes from its nucleus.

Lesson Assessment Answer Key

Arrange the following electrons into their proper shells.

5.

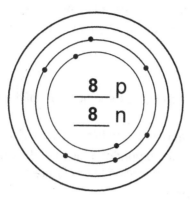

Oxygen: 8p, 8n, 8e

6.

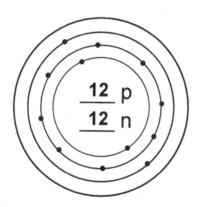

Magnesium: 12p, 12n, 12e

Learning Coach Guide
Lesson 2: The Periodic Table of Elements

Become familiar with the organization of the Periodic Table of the Elements. Elements are grouped by properties. For example, elements that are metals are clustered in the table. Explore the relationship between subatomic particles and atomic mass. Your student will gain in-depth knowledge by adopting and researching one particular element of his choice.

Lesson Objectives

- Explain that all the elements are organized in the Periodic Table of the Elements according to their chemical properties.
- Find the number of protons, electrons, and neutrons in an atom using its atomic number (the number of protons) and mass number (the number of protons and neutrons).
- Describe the common properties of metals (for example, they have luster, are bendable, and are good conductors of heat and electricity).
- Describe the common properties of nonmetals (for example, they are dull, brittle, and are poor conductors of heat and electricity).

PREPARE

Approximate lesson time is 60 minutes.

Materials

For the Student
  🖳 Atomic Calculations
  🖳 Periodic Table of the Elements

For the Adult
  🖳 Atomic Calculations Answer Key

Lesson Notes

All atoms have the same basic structure, but the atoms of all the different elements have different numbers of protons, electrons, and neutrons. When an atom is in a neutral electrical state, it has the same number of protons and electrons.

Atomic Number and Mass Number

The total number of protons in an atom is the *atomic number*. For example, hydrogen atoms have 1 proton and no neutrons, so the atomic number of hydrogen is 1. The total number of protons and neutrons in an atom is called the *mass number*. You can find the number of neutrons in any atom by subtracting the atomic number from the mass number. Lithium, for example, has a mass number of 7 and an atomic number of 3. Therefore, lithium has 4 neutrons. An *isotope* of a particular atom has the same number of protons and electrons as usual, but a different number of neutrons. Lithium has several isotopes, all of which have 3 protons but different numbers of neutrons.

In the accepted atomic model, a "cloud" of negatively charged electrons surrounds a positively charged nucleus that contains protons and neutrons. The electron cloud accounts for most of the atom's size, but the nucleus holds most of the atom's mass. This is because electrons have very little mass compared to protons and neutrons.

Atoms are so tiny that they don't have much mass. Atomic mass, therefore, is not measured in grams. Scientists use a much smaller unit of measurement called an *atomic mass unit*, or *u*. To find an element's mass number, round off the atomic mass to the nearest whole number. For example, the atomic mass of oxygen is 15.999 u. Therefore, oxygen's mass number is 16. This gives a good estimate for many atoms.

The Periodic Table of the Elements and the Symbols of Elements

There are more than 100 elements. Some are natural and some are man-made. These elements combine in millions of ways to make compounds. In the early 1800s, Swedish chemist Jons Jakob Berzelius gave each known element a letter symbol. Chemists still use these symbols as a type of shorthand. The first letter of an atomic symbol is always capitalized. The second letter, if there is one, is always lower case. Chemists also use these symbols to write the names of compounds. The symbol for sodium chloride, for example, is NaCl. In 1869, Russian scientist Dimitry Mendeleev first organized the elements into a table. In The Periodic Table of the Elements, each element has its own square. The element's name and symbol appear within this square. The atomic number of each element may be written above its symbol. Atomic mass may be written below the element's name.

Organization of the Periodic Table

The elements in the periodic table are listed in order by atomic number. You read the periodic table the same way you do words on a page--from left to right and top to bottom. Each horizontal row is called a *period*. The properties of the elements show a repeating, or *periodic*, pattern. This periodic pattern also shows up in the vertical columns. Elements in the vertical columns have similar properties and are called *groups*. Elements in one group combine or react in similar ways with other elements of other groups. For example, members of the fluorine (F), chlorine (Cl), and bromine (Br) group all react in similar ways with members of the lithium (Li), sodium (Na), and potassium (K) group. There are three general classes of elements: metals, nonmetals, and metalloids.

Keywords and Pronunciation

Dimitry Mendeleev (dih-MEE-tree men-duh-LAY-uhf)

halogen (HA-luh-juhn) : An element that forms a salt when it reacts with other elements. Chlorine, a halogen, reacts with sodium to form common table salt (NaCl).

Jons Jakob Berzelius (youns YAH-kawp buhr-ZAY-lee-uhs)

malleable (MA-lee-uh-buhl) : Able to be hammered out. Aluminum is so malleable that it can be hammered out into a thin foil.

metal : An element that is shiny, a good conductor of electricity, and malleable. Aluminum is a metal.

metalloid (MEH-tl-oyd) : An element that contains properties of both metals and nonmetals. Silicon is a metalloid.

noble gas : An element that is unreactive and rarely forms compounds with other elements. Helium is a noble gas.

nonmetal : An element that is dull, a poor conductor of electricity, and brittle. Oxygen, the most abundant element in the Earth's crust, is a nonmetal.

TEACH
Activity 1: The Periodic Table (Online)
Instructions
Have your student read through the Explore on his own. Reinforce and explain difficult concepts as needed.

Explore Suggestions:
There are many activities that you can do to familiarize your student with the Periodic Table of the Elements. You may wish to try any of these:

1. Identify states of matter. Have your student color mercury and bromine blue for liquids. Color hydrogen, helium, nitrogen, oxygen, fluorine, neon, chlorine, argon, krypton, xenon, and radon red for gases. Color the elements 43, 61, and 93-114 yellow--these are man-made. Color the rest of the elements brown for solids.

2. Play Element-Bingo. Have your student make a bingo card with either element symbols or names. Cut the periodic table into pieces and select one element at a time. You can say the element name, symbol, atomic number, etc. Your student must use a periodic table to see if he has the element on his bingo card.

3. Have your student spell words with symbols. Have him spell the word using the element name and see if you can guess the word he has spelled. For example: BrICK would be bromine-iodine-carbon-potassium. Who can spell the longest word?

4. Look for elements named after planets, countries, people, and cities, states, countries, or universities. (Planets: uranium, neptunium, plutonium, mercury. People: einsteinium, nobelium, mendelevium, curium, rutherfordium, seaborgium. Places and universities: californium, francium, americium, berkelium).

5. Look for elements whose symbols are entirely different from the spelling of the word, such as tungsten and sodium. Find out about their symbols.

After this activity, check to see if your student can do the following:

- Explain that all the elements are organized in the Periodic Table of the Elements according to their chemical properties.
- Describe the common properties of metals (for example, they have luster, are bendable, and are good conductors of heat and electricity).
- Describe the common properties of nonmetals (for example, they are dull, brittle, and are poor conductors of heat and electricity).
- Find the number of protons, electrons, and neutrons in an atom using its atomic number (the number of protons) and mass number (the number of protons and neutrons).

If your student has difficulty with any of these concepts, you may wish to review the Explore with him and have him explain the key points on each screen.

Activity 2: Atomic Calculations *(Offline)*

Instructions

Teaching:

Your student should be able to complete this activity on his own. He will need the most assistance understanding how to calculate the number of neutrons. Have him round the atomic mass on the periodic table to the nearest whole number. Then, have him subtract the atomic number (number of protons) from this rounded number--an approximation of the mass number. This will provide the number of neutrons for the common isotope of the atom of the element. There may be exceptions to this rule, but the lesson will provide practice in these calculations.

Troubleshooting:

Make sure your student is clear on the arithmetical procedure for calculating neutrons. If needed, have him draw circles to illustrate the particles in an atom.

What to Expect:

Your student should be able to determine and calculate the number of protons, electrons, and neutrons in an atom of any isotope. In some cases the number may not be the most common isotope, but will be close.

Answers:

See Answer Key.

Activity 3: Adopt an Element *(Online)*

Instructions

Teaching:

Ask your student to describe properties of different elements (shiny, dull, malleable, etc.). Density, state of matter, and melting and boiling points are also properties. Each element has properties that distinguish it from other elements.

What to Expect:

Using the resources listed, your student should find all the information about his adopted element--and then some!

ASSESS

Lesson Assessment: The Periodic Table of Elements (*Online*)

Students will complete an offline assessment based on the lesson objectives. Print the assessment and have students complete it on their own. Use the answer key to score the assessment, and then enter the results online. The attached answer key is the most current and may not coincide with previously printed guides.

TEACH
Activity 4: More Elemental Stuff *(Online)*

Instructions

Teaching:

You may wish to visit this site with your child.

What to Expect:

Your student will see how elements have been featured in comic books of the past.

Safety

The Periodic Table of Comic Books site (referenced in the Beyond the Lesson activity) shows snippets of comic book stories that may include fighting.

Name _____   Date _____

Atomic Calculations Answer Key

It would be hard to find a tool as useful as The Periodic Table of the Elements. In addition to displaying the name, symbol, atomic number, and atomic mass of more than 100 known elements, the Periodic Table contains much more information that can be quickly read.

In an electrically balanced atom, the number of protons and electrons is the same. The atomic number on the Periodic Table tells you the number of protons an element has in the nucleus of any one atom. Therefore, the atomic number also tells you the number of *electron*s in any one atom. Study the illustration below.

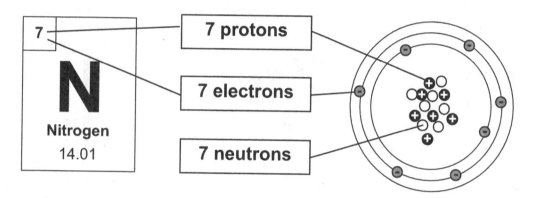

An atom of nitrogen has the same number of protons and electrons. How many neutrons does it have?

Figuring out the number of neutrons requires an easy extra step. At the bottom, under the element symbol, is a number. That number is the atomic mass. Remember that most of the mass in an atom comes from protons and neutrons in the nucleus. Round the atomic mass to the nearest whole number: 14, in this case. Then subtract the number of protons: 7. This number is often close to one or more common isotopes of the element. In some cases, however, an element has many different isotopes and therefore many different numbers of neutrons. The number at the bottom of the square gives you the average atomic mass of all the isotopes.

14 mass – 7 protons = 7 neutrons

Atomic Calculations Answer Key

Try this for yourself. Color the protons in this oxygen atom. Draw the electrons. Write the number of protons, electrons, and neutrons.

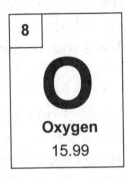

8
O
Oxygen
15.99

8 protons

8 electrons

8 neutrons

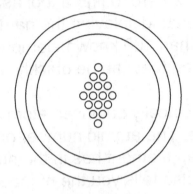

Write the number of protons, electrons, and neutrons in each atom.

3
Li
Lithium
6.94

Protons: **3**
Electrons: **3**
Neutrons: **4**

30
Zn
Zinc
65.37

Protons: **30**
Electrons: **30**
Neutrons: **35**

53
I
Iodine
126.90

Protons: **53**
Electrons: **53**
Neutrons: **74**

Use the Periodic Table to identify each element. Write the symbol, name, atomic number, and atomic mass in each square.

29
Cu
Copper
63.55

Protons: 29
Electrons: 29
Neutrons: 35

14
Si
Silicon
28.09

Protons: 14
Electrons: 14
Neutrons: 14

82
Pb
Lead
207.2

Protons: 82
Electrons: 82
Neutrons: 125

Atomic Calculations Answer Key

Use the Periodic Table to identify each element. Subtract the number of protons from the mass number to find the neutrons.

Atomic Mass (rounded)	Protons and Electrons	Neutrons	Element
12	6	**6**	**Carbon**
24	12	**12**	**Magnesium**
31	**15**	16	**Phosphorous**
59	**27**	32	**Cobalt**
35	17	**18**	**Chlorine**
197	79	**118**	**Gold**
226	88	**138**	**Radium**

Name _____   Date _____

Lesson Assessment Answer Key

The Periodic Table of Elements

Answers:

1. What is the Periodic Table of Elements?
   A table that has elements organized by properties and gives information about an element name, symbol, atomic mass, and atomic number.

2. Describe three characteristics of metals.
   Metals are shiny, good conductors of electricity, and are malleable.

3. Describe three characteristics of nonmetals.
   Nonmetals are dull, brittle, and poor conductors of electricity.

4. Name at least three classes of elements that are grouped together on the Periodic Table with similar properties.
   Answer should include at least three of the following: metals, nonmetals, metalloids, and noble gases.

5. How is it that the Periodic Table is useful to all scientists, no matter what language they speak?
   Key answer features: The organization of the Periodic Table of Elements makes it easy to use for scientists all over the world. Elements are grouped by properties and information is given in symbols and numbers, which can be understood without having to know different languages.

6. Find the number of protons, electrons, and neutrons in one atom of neon.
   ___10___ protons ___10___ electrons ___10___neutrons

7. Find the number of protons, electrons, and neutrons in one atom of titanium.
   Titanium: 22 protons, 22 electrons, 26 neutrons

Learning Coach Guide
Lesson 3: Compounds and Molecules

Compounds are formed when two or more elements join chemically. The elements lose their original chemical properties, and the new compound has completely new properties. A chemical formula provides information about the elements in a compound. Read and write chemical formulas and make compound models.

Lesson Objectives

- Use the chemical formula of a compound to identify the elements from which it is composed, and determine the number of each type of atom in the compound.
- Define a *compound* as a substance made of two or more elements.
- Explain that the properties of a compound differ from those of the elements that make up the compound.
- Recognize that elements combine in certain specific proportions to form compounds.

PREPARE

Approximate lesson time is 60 minutes.

Materials

For the Student
    📖 Modeling Molecules
For the Adult
    📖 Modeling Molecules Answer Key

Lesson Notes

Scientists have identified a little more than 100 elements. The atoms of these elements can combine to form millions and millions of chemical compounds, all with different properties. Nearly everything we encounter on a daily basis is a compound. *Compounds* form when two or more elements combine chemically. Interestingly, compounds do not have the same properties as the elements they are made of. *Sodium*, for example, is a soft metal that bursts into flames when it touches water. *Chlorine* is a yellow-green, poisonous gas. But when sodium atoms combine with chlorine atoms, they form ordinary table salt, or *sodium chloride*.

Earth's natural processes can form compounds. For example, silicon and oxygen combine within the Earth's crust to form the mineral *quartz*. Iron reacts with oxygen to form *hematite,* an iron ore. Living things also form compounds. Using photosynthesis, plants make their food in the form of a sugar compound called *glucose,* using carbon dioxide and water. Your digestive system chemically breaks down the compounds in your food so your body can use them.

Chemical Formulas of Compounds

Elements combine to form compounds, but they don't combine randomly. The atoms in each compound come together in certain proportions. *Carbon dioxide*, for example, has two atoms of oxygen and one atom of carbon. *Carbon monoxide* has one atom of oxygen and one atom of carbon. To keep all these compounds straight, scientists use chemical formulas to represent the names of compounds. A chemical formula for a compound is written with atomic symbols and numbers. The atomic symbols tell what elements are in a compound. The subscripted numbers tell how many atoms of each element are in the compound. If there is no subscript after an atomic symbol, it means there is only one atom of that element in the compound. The chemical formula for the compound water, for example, is written as H_2O. The H and O represent the elements hydrogen and oxygen. The subscript 2 beside the H indicates that there are 2 atoms of hydrogen in a molecule of water. The absence of a subscript after the O indicates that there is only 1 atom of oxygen.

Keywords and Pronunciation

subscript : The number displayed to the bottom right of a symbol that tells how many atoms of that element are present in a compound. In the chemical formula H_2O, the number 2 is the subscript.

TEACH
Activity 1: Elements Get Together--Chemically *(Online)*

Instructions
Have your student read through the Explore on his own. Reinforce and explain difficult concepts as needed.

Explore Suggestions:
Check your student's understanding by asking the following questions.

1. A substance made of two or more elements is a _____ . (compound)
2. What is the smallest part of a compound? (a single molecule)
3. What, if anything, can a molecule be broken into? (atoms)
4. What does a subscript mean in a formula? (It tells the number of atoms of a particular element in one molecule of the compound.)
5. Which is the formula for a compound of one atom of carbon and four atoms of hydrogen? (D)

   A. C4H

   B. CH

   C. CaH4

   D. CH4

After this activity, check to see if your student can do the following:

- Define a compound as a substance made of two or more elements bound together in molecules.
- Explain that the properties of a compound differ from those of the elements that make up the compound.
- Recognize that elements combine in certain specific, whole-number proportions to form compounds.
- Use the chemical formula of a compound to identify the elements from which it is composed and determine the number of each type of atom in the compound.

If your student has difficulty with any of these concepts, you may wish to review the Explore with him and have him explain the key points on each screen.

Safety

Keep your student away from poisonous products.

Activity 2: Modeling Molecules *(Offline)*
Instructions
Teaching:

Review subscripts. Subscripts tell how many atoms of an element are in one molecule of a compound. The subscript is written to the right and below the symbol of the element it is describing. If there is no subscript that means there is just one atom of that element in the molecule. No subscript does not mean zero atoms. Explain that if there were zero atoms of an element in a molecule, why would we bother writing the symbol at all?

What to Expect:

Your student should be able to write a chemical formula for a compound and identify the elements and their amounts in that compound. He should be able to construct a model of a compound with clay. His models may not show the atoms arranged correctly, so it is important to go over the answer key with him.

Answers:

See answer key.

ASSESS

Lesson Assessment: Compounds and Molecules *(Online)*

Students will complete an offline assessment based on the lesson objectives. Print the assessment and have students complete it on their own. Use the answer key to score the assessment, and then enter the results online. The attached answer key is the most current and may not coincide with previously printed guides.

TEACH
Activity 3: Surrounded by Compounds *(Online)*
Instructions
Teaching:

Discuss where to find names of compounds in products--they are usually written on the label in the list of ingredients.

Safety:

Keep your student away from poisonous products.

What to Expect:

Your student should be able to identify elements in compounds based on the compound name. Do not expect your student to name elements in compounds that do not have obvious names, unless he first researches the compounds.

Name _____   Date _____

Modeling Molecules Answer Key

Write the name and amounts of each element in each formula.

1. NaCl **Sodium (1), Chlorine (1)** _____

2. H_2SO_4 **Hydrogen (2), Sulfur (1), Oxygen (4)** _____

3. $CuSO_4$ **Copper (1), Sulfur (1), Oxygen (4)** _____

4. $C_6H_{12}O_6$ **Carbon (6), Hydrogen (12), Oxygen (6)** _____

Write the chemical formula for each molecule pictured below.

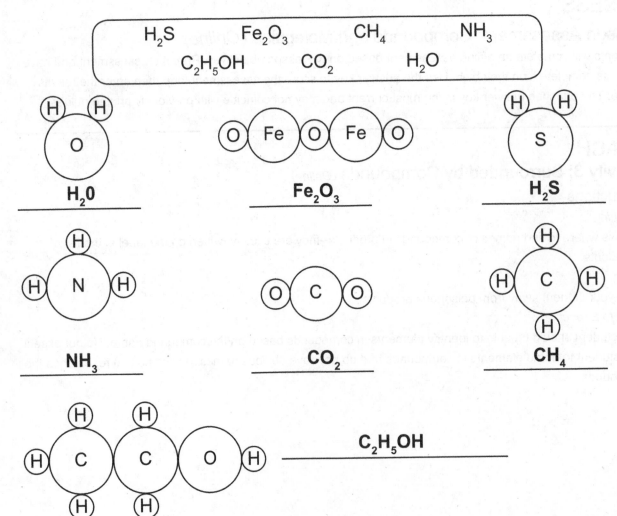

H_2S Fe_2O_3 CH_4 NH_3
C_2H_5OH CO_2 H_2O

H_2O

Fe_2O_3

H_2S

NH_3

CO_2

CH_4

C_2H_5OH

Lesson 3: Compounds and Molecules

Modeling Molecules Answer Key

Use clay and the key to make a model of one molecule of each compound. Use resources from this lesson to make sure the atoms are arranged correctly in each molecule.

KEY:
Blue = oxygen
Yellow = nitrogen
Green = hydrogen
Red = carbon

N_2
O_2
H_2O
CO_2
NH_3
CH_4

Challenge Models:
Can you arrange the atoms in the correct way?

C_3H_8
$C_6H_{12}O_6$

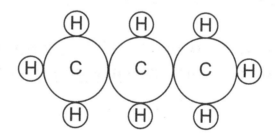

C_3H_8

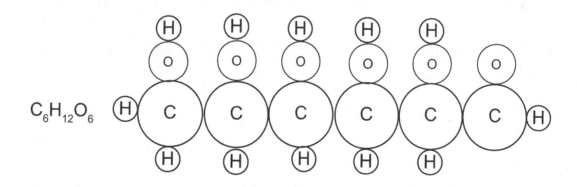

$C_6H_{12}O_6$

Name _____ Date _____

Lesson Assessment Answer Key

1. What is a compound? **A compound is a substance made of** **two or more elements joined in a chemical reaction.**

_____

2. What happens to the properties of atoms when they are joined through a chemical reaction to form a compound? Give an example. _____
The properties of atoms change when they are joined **chemically to make compounds. Suggested example: Sodium** **is a soft metal that explodes when it touches water. Chlorine** **is a yellow-green poisonous gas. When they are joined** **chemically, they make table salt, which is not poisonous.**

3. What does it mean when a symbol in a chemical formula is not followed by a subscript? **There is just one atom of that element** **in a molecule of that compound.**

4. How is the formula of a compound useful? **The formula tells** **how many elements are combined in a compound and in** **what amounts.**

5. Write the formula for a compound containing one atom of sodium, one atom of oxygen, and one atom of hydrogen. **NaOH**

6. Write the formula for a compound containing two atoms of aluminum and three atoms of sulfur. **Al_2S_3**

Learning Coach Guide
Lesson 4: Chemical Reactions

When substances engage in a chemical reaction, one or more poroducts form. Atoms are rearranged and the products have new chemical properties. Light energy, heat energy, release of gas, and the formation of a new solid are indications of a chemical reaction. Other reactions involove the input of energy, often heat energy. Chemical reactions can be written as chemical equations. A balanced equation shows the same number of atoms in the products as in the reactants. Observe a chemical reaction and work with chemical equations.

Lesson Objectives

- Identify the reactants and products in a chemical equation.
- Match chemical equations to word equations.
- Recognize that in chemical reactions the original atoms rearrange themselves into new combinations, and that the resulting products have properties differing from those of the reacting compounds.
- Recognize that for every chemical reaction the number of atoms of each element must be the same for both the reactants and the products.

PREPARE

Approximate lesson time is 60 minutes.

Advance Preparation

- Prepare iron acetate. Remove any soap from the steel wool with water. Fill one half of a jar with steel wool. Add vinegar so that is covers the steel wool. Label the jar "Iron Acetate." Leave the jar undisturbed for 5 days.

Materials

For the Student
- 💻 Reaction!
  ammonia
  jar - small (2)
  steel wool
  vinegar
  safety goggles
  spoon - tablespoon
- 💻 Chemical Equations
- 💻 Periodic Table of the Elements
  household item - calculator
  household item - crayons, 64 box
  household item - paper

For the Adult
- 💻 Chemical Equations Answer Key

Lesson Notes

When substances go through a chemical change they form compounds. And when substances combine chemically, the cause of the change can be found in the atoms of the substances. Their atoms form a *chemical bond*. In a chemical bond, the atoms of one substance share some electrons with atoms of the other substance. The resulting electrical attraction is a chemical bond and is what holds the atoms in the compound together.

As two chemicals combine to form a compound, the chemical bonds between the atoms in each chemical break. Then, new bonds form between different atoms. This is called a *chemical change* or *chemical reaction*. You can't see chemical bonds breaking or forming. However, you know when a chemical reaction is happening because you can see the evidence. When a substance burns, a chemical reaction is taking place. In the 1700s, French chemist Antoine Lavoisier showed that as a substance burns it combines with oxygen in the air to form other gases, leaving a small amount of ash behind. It might look as though the fire destroyed the matter, but the matter actually just changed form. Thanks to Lavoisier and other scientists, we now know that matter is never created or destroyed.

The substances involved in a chemical reaction are called *reactants*. The substances that form are called *products*. If you weigh the reactants before you combine them and then weigh the products, the reactants and products will have the same mass. This holds true for any physical or chemical change.

Expressing Chemical Reactions

There are several ways to express a chemical reaction. You can use a *word equation*, which is similar to a math equation. A quicker way to express a chemical reaction is with a *chemical equation*, which uses chemical formulas instead of words.

Word Equations: In a word equation, the name of the reactants goes on the left of the arrow and the name of the products goes on the right of the arrow. An example of a word equation is hydrogen + oxygen --> water. The arrow means *reacts to produce*, *gives*, or *yields*. If there is more than one reactant or product, they are separated by a plus sign. This only tells us the substances involved, not their amounts.

Chemical Equations: Hydrogen and oxygen are elements that exist naturally as molecules with two atoms. Their chemical formulas are H_2 and O_2. The formula for water is H_2O. You would think that the logical chemical equation for water would be $H_2 + O_2$ --> H_2O, but the problem with this equation is that it is not balanced. In a *balanced chemical equation*, the numbers of atoms must be the same in the reactants and the products. This is because during chemical reactions matter is neither created nor destroyed and chemical elements are not changed into other ones. The mass of the reactants must equal the mass of the products. This very important principle is called *conservation of matter*.

You can balance the elements in a chemical equation using something called a *coefficient*. A coefficient is a number placed in front of a chemical formula to show that there is more than one molecule of the compound. Two molecules of water, for example, would be written as $2H_2O$. In this example, the large number 2 is the coefficient. When a formula has no coefficient, we can assume that there is only one molecule of the compound. If you put a 2 in front of the H_2O in the chemical equation for water, the oxygen atoms become balanced: $H_2 + O_2$ --> $2H_2O$. But now the hydrogen atoms are unbalanced. You would need to place a 2 in front of the H_2 to balance the equation: $2H_2 + O_2$ --> $2H_2O$.

Keywords and Pronunciation
Antoine Lavoisier (AN-twahn lahv-WAHZ-yay)

TEACH
Activity 1: Chemical Reactions (Online)
Instructions
Have your student read through the Explore on his own. Reinforce and explain difficult concepts as needed.

Explore Suggestions:
Check your student's understanding by asking the following questions:
1. What are some clues that a chemical reaction has taken place? (Emission of light and heat energy, color changes, bubbling, and formation of a new solid or precipitate)
2. In a chemical equation, what is the name for the items that react? (reactants)
3. In a chemical equation, what is the name for the substance that is produced? (product)
4. Try describing this chemical equation in words: $CaO + CO_2 \rightarrow CaCO_3$ (Calcium oxide and carbon dioxide react to form calcium carbonate.)

Screen 7: Practice balancing chemical equations with this ChemBalancer.
http://www.dun.org/sulan/chembalancer/

After this activity, check to see if your student can do the following:
- Identify the reactants and products in a chemical equation.
- Match chemical equations to word equations.
- Recognize that in chemical reactions the original atoms rearrange themselves into new combinations, and that these new combinations have properties differing from those of the reacting compounds.
- Recognize that for every chemical reaction the number of atoms of each element must be the same for both the reactants and the products.

If your student has difficulty with any of these concepts, you may wish to review the Explore with him and have him explain the key points on each screen.

Activity 2: Reaction! (Offline)
Instructions
Teaching:
Discuss what clues tell you that a chemical reaction has taken place. (Light, heat, cooling, color changes, bubbling, and formation of a new solid are all evidence of a chemical reaction.) Discuss instances where your student may have seen a chemical reaction take place. Closely supervise your student during this activity.

Troubleshooting:
Be sure to remove all soap from the steel wool. Wear safety goggles and do not smell or taste any of the substances used in this activity. Do not play with the precipitate.

What to Expect:
Combining iron acetate and ammonia will produce a green precipitate. It may also have the consistency of a blob. Your student should understand that the mass of the blob and any other gases that escaped during the reaction equals the mass of the two liquids he combined.

Answers:
1. The two liquids reacted chemically and formed a green blob.
2. A color change to dark green and a precipitate was formed.
3. The reactants are iron acetate and ammonium hydroxide.
4. The products are iron hydroxide and ammonium acetate.
5. Their masses would be the same.

Safety

Wear safety goggles during this activity.

Do not smell, taste, or touch any of the reactants or products.

Wash all remaining solutions down the sink with lots of water after the activity.

Activity 3: Chemical Equations *(Offline)*

Instructions

Teaching:

Review chemical equations and how to balance them. Remind your student that an equation is balanced when there is the same number of atoms on one side of the equation as there is on the other. Coefficients are used to balance equations. Multiply the coefficient by the subscript to figure out how many atoms there are of that particular element. For example: $2O_2$ means there are four oxygen atoms present.

Troubleshooting:

Your student may find this easier if done concretely. Encourage your student to model the equation or draw individual atoms on paper.

What to Expect:

Your student should be able to write and balance a simple chemical equation. The equations in this lesson increase in complexity. Your student should be able to complete the first few of each exercise without assistance.

Answers:

See answer key.

ASSESS

Lesson Assessment: Chemical Reactions (*Online*)

Students will complete an offline assessment based on the lesson objectives. Print the assessment and have students complete it on their own. Use the answer key to score the assessment, and then enter the results online. The attached answer key is the most current and may not coincide with previously printed guides.

Name _____ Date _____

Chemical Equations

Chemical equations are a shorthand way of describing chemical reactions. A chemical equation is not finished, though, until it is balanced. A balanced equation has *the same number of atoms on the reactants' side as it has on the products' side.*

A. Count the number of atoms of each element on each side of the equation.
B. Use coefficients to balance the numbers of atoms.
C. Check your work by counting the numbers of atoms on each side of the equation again.

1. $\underline{2}H_2 + O_2 \rightarrow \underline{2}H_2O$ (water)
2. $\underline{2}Na + Cl_2 \rightarrow \underline{2}NaCl$ (sodium chloride)
3. $\underline{2}Fe + O_2 \rightarrow \underline{2}FeO$ (iron oxide)
4. $\underline{6}C + \underline{6}H_2O \rightarrow C_6H_{12}O_6$ (glucose)
5. $\underline{6}CO_2 + \underline{6}H_2O \rightarrow C_6H_{12}O_6 + \underline{6}O_2$ (glucose and oxygen)

With practice, you can learn to write chemical equations. Read the word equations below, then write their chemical equations. Make sure your equations balance. Chemical formulas that you may need are also listed.

6. Nitrogen and hydrogen yield ammonia.
   Nitrogen: N_2
   Hydrogen: H_2
   Ammonia: NH_3
   $N_2 + 3H_2 \rightarrow 2NH_3$ _____

7. Magnesium and oxygen yield magnesium oxide.
   Magnesium: Mg
   Oxygen: O_2
   Magnesium oxide: MgO

   $2Mg + O_2 \rightarrow 2MgO$ _____

Chemical Equations

8. Bromine and potassium iodide yield potassium bromide and
   iodine.

   Bromine: Br_2
   Potassium Iodide: KI
   Potassium bromide: KBr
   Iodine: I_2
   $Br_2 + 2KI \rightarrow 2KBr + I_2$

Challenge

Below is the chemical equation for photosynthesis, the process by
which plants use energy from the sun to make food. Rewrite the
equation for photosynthesis and balance it, if you can.

$CO_2 + H_2O + light \rightarrow C_6H_{12}O_6 + O_2$

$6CO_2 + 6H_2O + light \rightarrow C_6H_{12}O_6 + 6O_2$

Name _____   Date _____

Lesson Assessment Answer Key

1. In the following equation, which are the reactants and which are the products?

$$2H_2 + O_2 \rightarrow 2H_2O$$

Reactants: **hydrogen, oxygen**
Products: **water**

2. Match the chemical equations to the word equations.

$H_2 + Cl_2 = 2HCl$ Iron and sulfur react to yield iron sulfide.

$Ca + 2H_2O = Ca(OH)_2 + H_2$ Hydrogen and chlorine react to yield hydrochloric acid.

$Fe + S = FeS$ Mercury and oxygen react to yield mercuric oxide.

$2Hg + O_2 = 2HgO$ Calcium and water react to yield calcium hydroxide and hydrogen.

$CH_4 + O_2 = CO_2 + H_2O$

3. During this lesson, you observed a chemical reaction between ammonium hydroxide and iron acetate. Describe the properties of the products and of the reactant. _____
The reactants were a clear colored liquid and the product was a green solid.

4. How do you know when a chemical equation is balanced?
When the number of atoms of each element is the same for both the reactants and the products.

_____

Learning Coach Guide
Lesson 5: Acids and Bases

Substances may be acidic, basic, or neutral. Acids have certain properties--they taste sour and are corrosive when strong. Bases feel slippery and taste bitter. The strength of an acid or base is measured using the pH scale. Use this scale to find out if common solutions are acids or bases.

Lesson Objectives

- Use the pH Scale to determine whether a solution is acidic or basic.
- Describe properties of acids (for example, acids taste sour, are corrosive, and contain the element hydrogen).
- Describe properties of bases (for example, bases taste bitter and feel slippery when dissolved in water).
- Demonstrate mastery of the skills taught in this lesson.

PREPARE

Approximate lesson time is 60 minutes.

Materials

For the Student

    📖 Testing Acids and Bases

    ammonia - weak

    aspirin tablet

    cup, plastic (8)

    lemon juice

    litmus paper

    milk of magnesia

    soft drink

    vinegar - white

    graduated cylinder

    soap

    spoon

    tape - masking

    food - head of red cabbage

    strainer - or sieve

Optional

    coffee filter

    household item - food processor or knife

    household item - saucepan or 500 mL beaker

    jar, storage

    rubbing alcohol

For the Adult

    📖 Testing Acids and Bases Answer Key

Lesson Notes

Chemical compounds may be *acidic*, *basic*, or *neutral*.

Acids

All acids have some common properties. They all contain hydrogen, they all taste sour or tart, and they are all corrosive when strong. One of the properties of acids is that they react strongly with many metals. Some can react so strongly that they eat away, or *corrode*, the metal. Corrosion is a chemical reaction. When metal corrodes, a compound made of a metal and a nonmetal results, and hydrogen gas is released. As you will read, strong bases corrode, too.

Some acids are weak and some are strong. Strong acids react more quickly and have a greater effect on the substances they touch. The citric acid in citrus fruits, for example, is weak. Strong acids, however, can damage or burn your skin.

Many common items are acidic. They are products we use every day, including foods, cleaners, and medicines. *Sulfuric acid* is one of the most widely used chemicals in the world--it's the acid in car batteries, which is why it is sometimes called *battery acid*. Sulfuric acid is also used to make fertilizers, plastics, and paper. *Hydrochloric acid* is very strong acid that people use to clean the surfaces of concrete or steel. Your stomach also produces hydrochloric acid to help break down your food during digestion.

Bases

Bases are another group of important chemical compounds. Bases taste bitter instead of sour or tart. Strong bases can corrode materials. Bases are usually solids, but they dissolve in water and feel slippery because they react with the oil on your skin. Like strong acids, though, strong bases can damage your skin.

Many household products are basic. Soaps, detergents, and shampoos are all bases. The most widely used base is a strong compound, *sodium hydroxide*, called *lye*. It is used in oven cleaners and drain cleaners to break down grease. People put *calcium hydroxide*, often called *slaked lime*, on lawns and gardens where the soil is too acidic for proper plant growth. The calcium hydroxide base reacts with the acids in the soil to make the soil less acidic and more basic. Your blood is even a weak base.

Measuring Acids and Bases

A measurement called *pH* tells how acidic or basic a substance is. We measure pH with a numbered scale that ranges from 0 to 14. Solutions with a pH of less than 7 are *acidic*. Solutions with a pH greater than 7 are *basic*. Pure water has a pH of 7 and is considered *neutral*--it is neither acidic nor basic. Pure water is exactly in the middle of the scale. The lower the number on the pH scale, the stronger the acid. An acid that has a pH of 1 is much stronger than an acid that has a pH of 6. The opposite holds true for bases. The higher the number on the pH scale, the stronger the base.

One way to find the pH of a substance is to use a pH meter. A *pH meter* makes electrical measurements of a solution and gives a digital reading of the solution's pH. Another way is to use an indicator. An *indicator* is a substance that goes through various color or shade changes depending on the pH of the solution you are testing. An indicator takes on one color when you place it in an acid and another color when you place it in a base. Indicators are added to blue and red litmus paper. Acids turn blue litmus paper red, and bases turn red litmus paper blue. With other types of indicators, such as the strips used to test the pH of a swimming pool, you compare the color of the strip to a color chart. Each color on the chart represents a different pH.

Keywords and Pronunciation

base : compound that produces hydroxide ions in solution with water, reacts with an acid to form a salt, captures hydrogen ions, and donates an electron pair to form a chemical bond

acid : A substance that is characterized by sour taste and has a pH of less than 7. Ascorbic acid is found in citrus fruits such as lemons and oranges.

ascorbic (uh-SKOR-bihk)

bases : substance that is characterized by a bitter taste, slippery feel, and a pH of greater than 7

indicator : A dye that can be used to show the pH level of a solution. Litmus paper contains an indicator.

neutralize : To reduce the acidity of a substance with a base, and vice versa. Antacid tablets neutralize the acid in your stomach.

pH : A scale that measures the acidity or baseness of a solution. A substance is classified as an acid if it has a pH of less than 7.

TEACH
Activity 1: Acids and Bases *(Online)*
Instructions
Have your student read through the Explore on his own. Reinforce and explain difficult concepts as needed.

Explore Suggestions:
Check your student's understanding by asking the following questions:

1. The strengths of acids and bases is described by what scale? (pH)
2. Which numbers on the pH scale represent acids? (0-7)
3. Which numbers on the pH scale represent bases? (7-14)
4. What number on the pH scale represents a neutral solution? (7)
5. Which is being described, acid or base: feels slippery, tastes bitter, turns litmus paper blue? (base)

After this activity, check to see if your student can do the following:

- Describe properties of acids (for example, acids taste sour, are corrosive when strong, and contain the element hydrogen).
- Describe properties of bases (for example, bases taste bitter, are corrosive when strong, and feel slippery when dissolved in water).
- Use the pH Scale to determine whether a solution is acidic or basic.

If your student has difficulty with any of these concepts, you may wish to review the Explore with him and have him explain the key points on each screen.

Activity 2: Testing Acids and Bases *(Offline)*
Instructions
Teaching: Review the characteristics of acids and bases. Explain that an indicator such as litmus paper tells if a solution is an acid or a base by changing color. Solutions that are more acidic turn the paper red. Solutions that are more basic turn the paper blue. Supervise your student during this activity.

Troubleshooting: Do not allow your student to taste or smell any of the solutions. Wear safety goggles.

What to expect: The litmus paper will turn red in the presence of an acid and blue in the presence of a base. Your student should understand the significance of the color change and be able to identify solutions as acids or bases.

Answers:
See answer key.

Safety
Wear safety goggles. Do not taste or smell any of the solutions used in this activity.

ASSESS

Lesson Assessment: Acids and Bases (*Online*)
Students will complete an offline assessment based on the lesson objectives. Print the assessment and have students complete it on their own. Use the answer key to score the assessment, and then enter the results online. The attached answer key is the most current and may not coincide with previously printed guides.

TEACH

Activity 3. Optional: Cabbage Juice Indicator (*Offline*)
Instructions
Teaching: If needed, review the function of an indicator.

Troubleshooting: The cabbage juice indicator will have a strong odor.

What to Expect: The cabbage juice indicator will change color depending on the presence of an acid or a base.

Name _____   Date _____

Testing Acids and Bases

Litmus paper is a tool chemists use to determine whether a solution is an acid, a base, or is neutral. It is dipped into a solution and then removed. If the color of the litmus changes to red, the solution is acidic. If it changes to blue, it is basic. If it does not change color, the solution is neutral.

Use litmus paper as an indicator to test for acids and bases.

Hypothesis
From the following list of materials, predict which are acids and which are bases: white vinegar, lemon juice, weak ammonia solution, liquid soap, soft drink, milk of magnesia, aspirin, water.
Accept any reasonable hypothesis. _____

_____

_____

_____

Materials
litmus paper
8 plastic cups
graduated cylinder
spoon
masking tape
white vinegar
water

lemon juice
weak ammonia solution
liquid soap
soft drink
milk of magnesia
aspirin tablet
eyedropper

LAB SAFETY: Wear safety goggles during this activity. Do not smell or taste any of the solutions you test.

Testing Acids and Bases

Procedure
1. Use masking tape to make a label for each cup: vinegar, lemon juice, ammonia, liquid soap, soft drink, milk of magnesia, aspirin, water.
2. Crush the aspirin tablet in 120 mL of water.
3. Use the cylinder to add 5 mL of each solution to the cups.
4. Use the eyedropper to place a few drops of a solution between your thumb and forefinger, then rub your fingers together. Does the solution feel slippery?
5. Wash your hands.
6. Dip one piece of litmus paper into the first cup. Record your results on the chart.
7. Repeat the test for each cup with a new piece of litmus paper each time.

Science Notebook:
Identify the variables in your experiment. Remember, the *independent variable* is what the experimenter changes in an experiment. The *dependent variable* is what happens because of the change.

Independent Variable: **the solutions tested**

Dependent Variable: **the color of the litmus paper or whether it is**
an acid, neutral, or base

Solution	Slippery Feel	Litmus Paper Color	Acid, Base, or Neutral?
White Vinegar	No	Red	Acid
Lemon Juice	No	Red	Acid
Ammonia	Yes	Blue	Base
Liquid Soap	Yes	Blue	Base
Soft Drink	No	Red	Acid
Milk of Magnesia	Yes	Blue	Base
Water	No	No color change	Neutral
Aspirin	No	Red	Acid

Testing Acids and Bases

Conclusion

1. Check your hypothesis. Which substances did you predict correctly? __Accept any reasonable answers.__

2. If you predicted any incorrectly, explain why you think this happened. __Accept any reasonable answers.__

Investigation Idea

Wet a cotton swab with your saliva. Touch the saliva to the paper to find out if your saliva is acidic or basic.

Name _____   Date _____

Lesson Assessment Answer Key

Consider the properties of acids and bases. Write True before each true statement. Write False before each false statement.

1. __True__ Acids will turn litmus paper red.
2. __False__ Acids taste bitter.
3. __False__ Bases taste sour.
4. __True__ Bases feel slippery.
5. __True__ Adding a base makes an acid less acidic.
6. __False__ Bases will turn litmus paper red.
7. __True__ Ammonia is a base.
8. __True__ Acids are corrosive.
9. __True__ Acids contain hydrogen.

Tell if the following substances are an acid, a base, or neutral.

10. ____base____ pH = 11
11. ____acid____ pH = 3
12. ____base____ pH = 14
13. ____acid____ pH = 2
14. __neutral__ pH = 7

15. Describe how one indicator is used to test whether something is an acid or a base. _____
    Litmus paper placed in a solution will turn either red or blue. Based on the pH scale, if it turns red, the solution is an acid. If it turns blue, the solution is a base.
    _____
    _____
    _____

Lesson Assessment Answer Key

16. As a scientist, you test a series of solutions to determine their pH. Your results are below.

Substance	pH
A	9
B	12
C	11
D	14

Which one of these solutions would be most effective at neutralizing a strong acid? Why?

Substance D because with a pH of 14, it is the strongest base, which makes it most effective at neutralizing strong acids.

Learning Coach Guide
Lesson 6: Identification of Compounds

The products of a chemical reaction can be identified by various tests. Iodine changes color in the presence of starch. Flames glow with different colors when in the presence of different metallic compounds. Learn about methods for identifying compounds, then investigate one method and observe another.

Lesson Objectives

- Name four types of evidence of a chemical reaction: Change in temperature, color change, release of a gas, and the formation of a precipitate.
- Describe one method of identifying a compound or element in a product of a chemical reaction.

PREPARE

Approximate lesson time is 60 minutes.

Advance Preparation

- If you don't already have it, you will need iodine for the Starch Search activity.

Materials

For the Student

    💻 Starch Search

      household item - apple

      iodine - Lugol's iodine solution or iodine tincture

      potato - white

      bread

      plate, paper

Lesson Notes

We've learned that in certain kinds of chemical reactions, the bond between some of the atoms breaks and the atoms form new chemical bonds. The substances that undergo a chemical reaction are called *reactants*. The results of the reaction are called *products*. When a chemical reaction takes place, at least one new product forms. The properties of the product are different from those of the reactants from which it was formed. Because the new compound has different properties, you can tell that the chemical reaction had taken place. Sometimes the products of a chemical reaction have a different color than the reactants. A new color shows that a new compound is present. Other evidence includes the release of a gas in the form of bubbles or an odor.

Releasing or Absorbing Energy

When a chemical reaction takes place, the reaction either releases energy or absorbs energy. One way to tell which is by measuring the temperature of the reactants. When wood burns, for example, energy is released (in the form of heat and light), and the temperature rises. Prior to the reaction, the energy was in the chemical bonds of the reactants. It was transformed when the bonds broke and reformed.

You can tell when a chemical reaction absorbs energy because the temperature of the reactants goes down. Imagine dropping an antacid tablet into a glass of water. If you measured the temperature of the water as it began to bubble, you would see the temperature drop.

Temperature change and the release of gas are good indications of a chemical reaction. But they do not *always* mean a chemical reaction is taking place. Temperature changes also occur when matter changes states from solid to liquid to gas.

Indicators of Chemical Reactions

Many tests use chemical indicators to reveal more about a specific chemical reaction. Sometimes you need more than one type of test to determine what elements are in a compound. Chemists often use specialized equipment that helps them determine unknown compounds. But you can also often figure out what new compounds have formed as products of a chemical reaction by using *indicators*. Indicators show the presence of some new or changed compound. For example, you can use a pH indicator, such as litmus paper, cabbage juice, or a pH meter, to see if the pH of a solution has changed.

You can test for the presence of starches using a solution of iodine. Starches occur naturally in potatoes and foods made with wheat, corn, and rice. If you drop IKI, an iodine solution, into a starch, the solution turns from brown to a deep purple--almost black.

Other tests can indicate if a certain chemical compound is present in a reactant or product. Because certain chemical compounds need oxygen to burn (to react), you can use a simple test to find out whether oxygen is a reactant. An extinguished fire that is still glowing will flare up again and begin to burn if you place it into a container full of oxygen.

You can use a flame test to determine whether a compound contains certain metals. For example, sodium chloride (table salt) burns with a bright yellow flame, indicating the presence of sodium. Boric acid turns flames green because it contains the element *boron*. Cream of tartar (a cooking ingredient) flames lilac because of its potassium content.

Another way to identify reactants and products is to add a substance that results in the formation of a solid, called a *precipitate*. During some reactions, a solid forms in the solution. This precipitate is often the product of a chemcial reaction between two liquid solutions.

Keywords and Pronunciation

precipitate (prih-SIH-puh-tayt) : A solid that forms as a result of a chemical reaction. A white solid precipitate may form when aluminum chloride is added to a substance that contains aluminum.

residue : A substance left over as a result of a chemical reaction. The black residue left over from burning fossil fuels or wood is carbon.

TEACH
Activity 1: Identifying Compounds (Online)

Instructions
Have your student read through the Explore on his own. Reinforce and explain difficult concepts as needed.

Explore Suggestions:
Check your student's understanding by asking the following questions:

Explore Suggestions:

Check your student's understanding by asking the following questions:

1. Why isn't temperature change always an indicator of a chemical change? (Because when things change state, such as from solid to liquid, there is a temperature change but the change is not chemical.)

2. Name an indicator that is used to test for starch. (iodine)

3. How do flame tests show whether there is a certain metal in a compound? (Metals give characteristic colors to the flame.)

After this activity, check to see if your student can do the following:

• Name four types of evidence of a chemical reaction: change in temperature, color change, release of a gas, and the formation of a precipitate.

• Describe one method of identifying a compound or element in a product of a chemical reaction.

If your student has difficulty with any of these concepts, you may wish to review the Explore with him and have him explain the key points on each screen.

Activity 2: Starch Search *(Offline)*
Instructions
Teaching:

Discuss how iodine can be used to detect starch. Ask your student if he remembers what color iodine changes when there is starch in a substance. If there is starch, it turns from brown to a deep purple-black.

Troubleshooting:

Wear safety goggles during this activity.

What to Expect:

The iodine will turn from orange-brown to dark purple-black on the potato and bread. It will not change color on the apple. Your student should understand that there is starch in the potato and bread, and not in the apple, based on the reaction of the iodine. Use an barely ripe apple, not an old soft one that contains a lot of starch

Answers:

Hypothesis: Accept any reasonable prediction.

Scientist Notebook: IV: the foods, DV: whether or not there is starch, Conclusion: whether or not there is starch

Observations: Iodine changes to deep purple-black on the bread and potato but there is no change on the apple.

Analysis: potato and bread

Conclusion: Iodine was placed on foods to determine whether there was starch in them. Iodine turned deep purple-black on the potato and bread, so that means there is starch in them. There must be no starch in the apple because the iodine did not change color.

Safety
Wear safety goggles during the Starch Search activity.

Activity 3: Flame Tests (Online)

Instructions

Teaching:

Flame tests can be used to determine whether a compound contains certain metals. A *salt* is a type of compound that is formed from a metal and non-metal. Table salt is made of the metal sodium and the non-metal chlorine. Table salt is just one type of salt. In the presence of certain metals, flames will burn a different color.

What to Expect:

Your student will see three examples of flame tests, each displaying a different color. He should understand that the different colors result from the presence of different metals in the compound that was ignited. The color of the flame can help determine what those metals are.

ASSESS

Lesson Assessment: Identification of Compounds (*Online*)

Students will complete an offline assessment based on the lesson objectives. Print the assessment and have students complete it on their own. Use the answer key to score the assessment, and then enter the results online. The attached answer key is the most current and may not coincide with previously printed guides.

Name _____   Date _____

Lesson Assessment Answer Key

Write True if the statement is true. Write False if the statement
is false.

1. __**False**__ A change in temperature is always an indicator
   of a chemical reaction.
2. __**True**__ A color change is an indicator of a chemical reaction.
3. __**False**__ A change in size is an indicator of a chemical reaction.
4. __**True**__ The release of gas is an indicator of a chemical reaction.
5. __**True**__ The formation of a precipitate is an indicator of a
   chemical reaction.
6. __**False**__ A change in state is an indicator of a chemical reaction.

7. Several methods can tell you whether there is a particular compound
   or element in a product of a reaction. Describe one method.
   Key answer features: iodine test for starch, flame test for
   metals or carbon, pH test for acids or bases, or a test in
   which a new solid or precipitate forms.

_____

Learning Coach Guide
Lesson 7: Molecules of Life

Our bodies must have certain organic compounds to function, grow, and develop. *Carbohydrates*, *proteins*, and *lipids* are three classes of these molecules. They are taken into the body with food. Learn about the structure and function of these organic molecules.

Lesson Objectives
- Define organic compounds as carbon-based, such as those produced by living things and certain others produced in chemistry laboratories.
- Define inorganic compounds as those that do not usually contain the element carbon.
- Recognize that living organisms are composed of mainly just a few elements: carbon, hydrogen, oxygen, and nitrogen.
- Describe the functions of proteins, lipids, and carbohydrates in human nutrition.

PREPARE

Approximate lesson time is 60 minutes.

Materials

For the Student
- 🖳 Carbohydrates, Proteins, and Lipids
- 🖳 Molecular Models
  - clay - blue
  - clay - green
  - clay - red
  - clay - yellow
  - toothpicks

For the Adult
- 🖳 Carbohydrates, Proteins, and Lipids Answer Key

Lesson Notes

Life is assocaiated with carbon compounds. Most compounds that contain carbon are called *organic compounds*. Compounds that have no carbon are called *inorganic compounds*. Even the simplest living thing is composed of a huge variety of organic compounds. But all these compounds are made up of just a few elements--mostly carbon, hydrogen, oxygen, and nitrogen. The atoms of these four elements can combine in countless ways to make organic molecules. There are three main types of organic molecules: carbohydrates, proteins, and lipids.

Carbohydrates

Carbohydrates are the main fuel that cells burn to get energy. Carbohydrates are in foods such as bread, pasta, rice, and potatoes. The simplest carbohydrate molecules are simple sugars. *Glucose* is a simple sugar found in many plants and animals. *Fructose* is a simple sugar found in fruits and honey. Cells get most of their energy from sugars, but our bodies take in and store larger carbohydrate molecules called *starches*. Starch molecules are made of many glucose molecules linked together. Your body can store starch molecules and break them down into glucose molecules.

Proteins

Proteins are the second major class of organic molecules. Proteins have many important jobs in your body. Proteins help form your skin and muscles. They help carry the oxygen in your blood to all parts of your body. Proteins also act as *enzymes*. They speed up chemical reactions in the cells of living things.

Just as starches are made of sugar molecules linked together, proteins are long chains of molecules called *amino acids*. Each protein has its own order of amino acids. The order gives the protein its chemical properties.

There are 20 naturally occurring amino acids. Each has a three-letter symbol. Combinations of amino acids are called *peptides*. Peptides that have more than 100 amino acids are proteins. These long chains of peptides do not usually stay straight. They fold, twist, and spiral to form three-dimensional structures.

As you digest foods high in protein, your body breaks down the protein into its different amino acids. Your body then uses the amino acids to build its own proteins.

Lipids

Lipids are the third major class of organic molecule. Lipids are better known as *fats* and *oils*. Like carbohydrates and proteins, lipids are long chains of smaller molecules. But unlike carbohydrates and proteins, lipids are insoluble. They do not dissolve well in water. Lipids insulate you from the cold and protect and cushion your nerves. They also supply the raw materials your body needs to build some of the chemical messengers called *hormones*. Lipids store more energy in their bonds than carbohydrates do.

Keywords and Pronunciation

carbohydrates (kahr-boh-HIY-drayts) : Substances made from carbon, oxygen, and hydrogen that provide energy to the body in the form of glucose. Pasta, bread, and rice are foods high in carbohydrates.

lipid (LIH-puhdz) : Substances that include fats and oils and provide the body with energy and material to build hormones. Lipids are found in foods containing fat.

proteins : Substances built from amino acids that function in many ways in the body. Proteins provide the body with material for forming new cells, skin, and muscles.

TEACH
Activity 1: The Molecules of Our Lives *(Online)*
Instructions
Have your student read through the Explore on his own. Reinforce and explain difficult concepts as needed.

Explore Suggestions:
Check your student's understanding by asking the following questions:

1. A compound that is found naturally in, or is produced by, living things and contains carbon is an _____ compound. (organic)
2. A compound that is not found in living things and usually does not contain carbon is an _____ compound. (inorganic)
3. What are the three main types of organic compounds? (carbohydrates, proteins, lipids)
4. Which foods are high in carbohydrates? Proteins? Lipids? (pastas, bread, rice; eggs, meat, dairy; fats and oils)

Screen 3: Ask your student how many atoms of carbon, hydrogen, and oxygen are in a single molecule of glucose. (Answer: 6, 12, and 6)

After this activity, check to see if your student can do the following:
- Define *organic compounds* as those naturally found in, or produced by, living things that contain the element carbon.
- Define *inorganic compounds* as those that do not come from living organisms and do not usually contain the element carbon.
- Recognize that living organisms are composed of mainly just a few elements: carbon, hydrogen, oxygen, and nitrogen.
- Describe the functions of proteins, lipids, and carbohydrates in human nutrition.

If your student has difficulty with any of these concepts, you may wish to review the Explore with him and have him explain the key points on each screen.

Activity 2: Review Carbohydrates, Proteins, and Lipids *(Offline)*
Instructions
Teaching:
Have your student return to the content at the beginning of the lesson to complete the activity.
What to Expect:
Your student should be able to describe the functions of carbohydrates, proteins, and lipids.
Answers:
See answer key.

Activity 3: Molecular Models *(Offline)*
Instructions
Teaching:
Carbohydrates, proteins, and lipids are the three classes of organic compounds. We take them in by eating. The carbohydrates, proteins, and lipids in our daily diet are called *nutrients*. It is important to eat a balanced diet to get the necessary nutrients into our bodies.
Carbohydrates, proteins, and lipids have specific molecular structures. All of them contain just four elements: carbon, hydrogen, nitrogen, and oxygen.
What to Expect:
Your student should be able to make a model of each type of organic molecule. He should also understand their roles in our body processes and name some foods in which they can be found.

Answers:

1. It is stored as fat.
2. Check that your student has identified carbohydrates (breads, pasta, rice, vegetables, sweets), proteins (nuts, meats, dairy), and lipids (oils, fats) accurately.

ASSESS

Lesson Assessment: Molecules of Life (*Online*)

Students will complete an offline assessment based on the lesson objectives. Print the assessment and have students complete it on their own. Use the answer key to score the assessment, and then enter the results online. The attached answer key is the most current and may not coincide with previously printed guides.

Name _____   Date _____

Carbohydrates, Proteins, and Lipids Answer Key

Use the table to compare carbohydrates, proteins, and lipids.
Then answer the questions.

	Carbohydrates	Proteins	Lipids
Structure	**Linked sugars**	**Long chains of amino acids**	**Long chains of molecules**
In what foods?	**Bread, pasta, potatoes, rice**	**Meats, beans, nuts, eggs, and dairy products**	**Fats and oils**
Purpose in the body	**Break down into glucose, which stores energy for cells to use**	**Build new cells, form skin and muscles, carry oxygen, and act as enzymes to speed up chemical reactions in the body**	**Insulate from cold, supply raw material to make hormones, and provide energy which is stored as fat until it can be used**

1. Organic compounds are found naturally in, or are produced by, living things and contain the element _____**carbon**_____ .

2. Compounds that do not come from living organisms and do not contain this element are called _____**inorganic**_____ compounds.

3. What four elements are the main components of living things?
carbon, nitrogen, hydrogen, oxygen

Name _____   Date _____

Lesson Assessment Answer Key

Molecules of Life

Answers:

1. Explain the difference between an organic and inorganic compound.
   An organic compound is found naturally in, or produced by, living things and contains carbon. An inorganic compound does not come from living things and usually does not contain carbon.

2. Proteins, carbohydrates, and lipids are which type of compound?
   organic compound

3. Most organic compounds are made of just four elements. What are they?
   hydrogen, oxygen, nitrogen, and carbon

4. Match the organic compound to its role in nutrition.

   c Carbohydrate

   a Protein

   d Lipid

   a. helps the body build new cells, as well as skin and muscles

   b. provides building material for strong bones and teeth

   c. provides the body with energy in the form of glucose

   d. insulates you from the cold and helps build hormones.

Learning Coach Guide
Lesson 8: Reaction Rates

Learn four ways to increase the rate of a chemical reaction. Explore two methods in particular: increasing temperature and increasing surface area.

Lesson Objectives
- Explain that all chemical reactions require a certain amount of energy in order to break existing bonds in the reactants and form new bonds in the products.
- Recognize that enzymes can act as catalysts to speed up chemical reactions in the human body.
- Identify four ways to increase the rate of a chemical reaction (increase the temperature, surface area, concentration, and add a catalyst).

PREPARE

Approximate lesson time is 60 minutes.

Advance Preparation
- You will need at least 6 fizzling antacid tablets, 3 balloons, and 3 plastic10-12oz bottles for the Quick Action Reaction activity. If you choose to complete the Flour Power activity, you will need a half gallon milk carton and rubber tubing.

Materials
For the Student

📖 Quick Action Reaction

bottle, plastic - 10, 12 oz soda

drinking glass - clear, 3

household item - cutting board

household item - fizzling antacid tablets (6)

household item - stopwatch

rock

thermometer, Celsius/Fahrenheit

balloon - 3 (blow up to stretch)

graduated cylinder

paper

spoon

water - tap, cold

water - tap, room temperature

Optional

> household item - aluminum foil
>
> household item - candle
>
> household item - flour
>
> household item - lighter or match
>
> household item - milk carton, half-gallon
>
> tubing, rubber
>
> funnel

For the Adult

> water - tap, hot

Lesson Notes

Chemical reactions take place when the molecules of the reactants collide. The molecules must be in just the right position and collide with just the right amount of energy. Intermediate chemcial compounds form, then the intermediate bonds break and form products. Otherwise, existing bonds won't break and new bonds won't form in the products. Different chemical reactions take different amounts of time. The time span of a reaction depends on the chemical nature of the reactants and the products. There are several ways to speed up the rate of a chemical reaction. These include increasing temperature, increasing concentration, increasing surface area, and using a catalyst.

Increasing Temperature

Raising the temperature of the reactants speeds up the rate of a chemical reaction in some cases. This is because it increases the energy level of the atoms in the molecules. When atoms have more energy, more will react when they collide. And since the molecules are moving faster, they collide more often. Having more high-energy collisions means having a faster reaction time.

Increasing Concentration

Increasing the *concentration* of the reactants will also speed up a chemical reaction. When reactants have a higher concentration, there are more molecules per unit volume. Therefore, more molecules can collide with each other and cause a reaction.

Increasing Surface Area

A third way to speed up the rate of a chemical reaction is to increase the surface area of the reactants. An increase in surface area means more of the reactants are exposed to each other. When more of the surface is exposed, more molecules can collide in a given time. Having more collisions means having a faster chemical reaction. Chemists often dissolve reactants in liquids to speed up a chemical reaction. Dissolving separates the reactants into individual molecules and increases the surface area.

Using a Catalyst

Many chemical reactions use a catalyst to speed up the rate without increasing the temperature, concentration, or surface area. A *catalyst* is a substance that increases the rate of a reaction but doesn't undergo any permanent change. Catalysts help reactions take place more quickly. The molecules of catalysts form temporary bonds with the molecules of the reactants. These temporary bonds help the other bonds break more easily. Catalysts lower the amount of energy that atoms and molecules need to react when they collide. They can also help move the molecules into the best positions to react with each other. In a chemical equation, the symbol for the catalyst is written above the arrow.

Keywords and Pronunciation

catalyst (KA-tl-uhst) : A substance that increases the rate of a reaction but doesn't get used up. To speed the decomposition of hydrogen peroxide into water and oxygen, use manganese dioxide as a catalyst.

concentration : The amount of something packed into a given space. The concentration of students on the bus increased when Jared and Sonya got on.

enzymes (EN-ziym) : A protein in the body. Some enzymes help break food down into usable nutrients during digestion. Enzymes in your saliva break down starch, starting the process of digestion.

surface area : The amount of space the outer face of an object takes up. To find the surface area of a rectangle, multiply the width times the height.

TEACH
Activity 1: Explore: Reaction Rates *(Online)*

Instructions

Have your student read through the Explore on his own. Reinforce and explain difficult concepts as needed.

Explore Suggestions:

Check your student's understanding by asking the following questions:

1. Adding a catalyst, increasing the temperature, increasing surface area, and increasing concentration are all ways of doing what? (speeding up a chemical reaction)
2. What kind of effect does adding a catalyst have on a reaction? (none, except its rate is increased)
3. Mary crushes a substance to a fine powder before combining it with another substance in a chemical reaction. What method has Mary used to speed up the reaction? (increase surface area)

After this activity, check to see if your student can:

- Explain that all chemical reactions require a certain amount of energy in order to break existing bonds in the reactants and form new bonds in the products.
- Identify four ways to increase the rate of a chemical reaction (increase the temperature, the surface area, the concentration, and add a catalyst).
- Recognize that enzymes act as catalysts to speed up chemical reactions in the human body.

If your student has difficulty with any of these concepts, you may wish to review the Explore with him and have him explain the key points on each screen.

Activity 2: Quick Action Reaction *(Offline)*
Instructions

Teaching:

There are several ways by which to speed up a chemical reaction. Discuss some reasons why you would want to make a chemical reaction faster.

Troubleshooting:

Your student should wear safety goggles during this activity. You will need to help your student place the balloon over the mouth of the bottle during the first investigation.

What to Expect:

The tablet will react faster in hot water. The powdered tablet will react faster than the whole tablet. Your student should observe and understand two factors that can speed up the rate of a chemical reaction: an increase in temperature and an increase in surface area.

If the tablets do not release gas when placed in tap water, add a few drops of vinegar to the tap water and try it again.

Answers:

Fill in the Blank:

1. catalyst
2. temperature
3. surface area
4. concentration

Experiment 1:

Scientist Notebook: The independent variable is the temperature of water. The dependent variable is the reaction time in seconds.

Analysis: Check your student's graph for accuracy. Make sure it shows that the hotter water caused a faster reaction.

Conclusion:

1. The rate increases, or speeds up.
2. Accept any reasonable answer.
3. Accept any reasonable answer based on your student's graph.
4. double

Experiment 2:

Scientist Notebook: The independent variable is the condition of the tablet. The dependent variable is the reaction time.

Analysis: Check your student's graph for accuracy. Make sure it shows that the powdered tablet underwent a faster reaction.

Conclusion:

1. It increases
2. Accept any reasonable answer based on your student's data.
3. Check to make sure that your student's answer is based on his data for both investigations.

Safety

Wear safety goggles during the Quick Action Reaction activity.

Use caution when handling hot water.

ASSESS

Lesson Assessment: Reaction Rates (*Online*)

Students will complete an offline assessment based on the lesson objectives. Print the assessment and have students complete it on their own. Use the answer key to score the assessment, and then enter the results online. The attached answer key is the most current and may not coincide with previously printed guides.

TEACH
Activity 3: Flour Power--Surface Area and Reactions *(Online)*
Instructions
Teaching:

Review the concept of *surface area* if needed.

Troubleshooting:

Follow all safety instructions here, and accompanying the activity, if you choose to do it. You may wish to have your student watch you and another adult do the activity so he can see the effects more clearly.

What to Expect:

When flour is blown through the tube and funnel, it will ignite in a much bigger flame than when a pile of flour is ignited. This is due to the increase in surface area.

Safety
The Flour Power activity involves flames. Please supervise your student.

The Flour Power activity must be done in a wide-open area.

Lesson Assessment Answer Guide

Reaction Rates

Answers:

1. Add a **catalyst** that is unaffected by the reaction.
2. Expose more of the reactant by increasing the **surface area**.
3. Pack in more of the reactant to increase the **concentration**.
4. Increase the **temperature** to allow the reaction to happen with more energy.

5. In order for a chemical reaction to take place, a certain amount of **D. energy** must be present.

6. Catalysts that speed up chemical reactions in the human body are called **B. enzymes**

Learning Coach Guide
Lesson 9: Unit Review and Assessment

By now your student should be very familiar with atomic structure and the periodic table. He will review these, as well as compounds, chemical reactions, and chemical equations. This is his chance to show his expertise in those areas.

Lesson Objectives

- Identify the three main parts of atoms as protons, electrons, and neutrons, and that protons have a positive charge, electrons a negative charge, and neutrons have no charge at all.
- Explain that all the elements are organized in the Periodic Table of the Elements according to their chemical properties.
- Use the pH Scale to determine whether a solution is acidic or basic.
- Describe the current model of the atom as a positively charged nucleus containing the protons and neutrons surrounded by electrons moving in certain regions within an "electron cloud".
- Recognize that in chemical reactions the original atoms rearrange themselves into new combinations, and that the resulting products have properties differing from those of the reacting compounds.
- Recognize that the atoms of an element are exactly alike and that each element is made of only one kind of atom.
- Describe the common properties of metals and nonmetals.
- Identify some common elements and compounds by both their chemical symbols and their formulas.
- Describe a *compound* as a substance made of two or more elements. Explain that the properties of a compound differ from those of the elements that make up the compound.
- Write chemical equations to show what happens in a chemical reaction.
- Explain that all chemical reactions require energy.
- Describe how reaction rates increase with temperature, surface area, concentration, and in the presence of a catalyst.
- Find the number of protons, electrons, and neutrons in an atom using its atomic number (the number of protons) and mass number (the number of protons and neutrons).
- Recognize that atoms of each element are exactly alike.
- Describe the common properties of metals (for example, they have luster, are bendable, and are good conductors of heat and electricity).
- Describe the common properties of nonmetals (for example, they are dull, brittle, and are poor conductors of heat and electricity).
- Define a *compound* as a substance made of two or more elements.
- Name four types of evidence of a chemical reaction: Change in temperature, color change, release of a gas, and the formation of a precipitate.
- Recognize that living organisms are composed of mainly just a few elements: carbon, hydrogen, oxygen, and nitrogen.
- Recognize that enzymes can act as catalysts to speed up chemical reactions in the human body.
- Demonstrate mastery of the skills taught in this unit.
- Identify some parts of the human endocrine system and their function (pituitary gland, thyroid gland, adrenal gland, and pancreas).

PREPARE

Approximate lesson time is 60 minutes.

Materials

For the Student

🖥 Question Review Table

TEACH

Activity 1: Professor Pete and the Interview *(Online)*

Instructions

Have your student read through the Explore on his own. Since this is a review, encourage him to return to any earlier lessons that might help him. Reinforce and explain difficult concepts as needed. If he has difficulty with any of these concepts, you may wish to review the Explore with him and have him explain the key points on each screen.

ASSESS

Unit Assessment: Chemistry *(Online)*

Please print the Periodic Table of Elements. Then print the Assessment for your student to complete. Have your student refer to the Periodic Table handout to complete the assessment. Enter the results online.

TEACH

Activity 2. Optional: Unit Assessment Review Table *(Online)*

Activity 3. Optional: ZlugQuest Measurement *(Online)*

Name _____ Date _____

Unit Assessment Answer Key
Chemistry

Choose the letter that best answers the question.

1. How are elements arranged in the Periodic Table?
   - (A) by their properties
   - B. alphabetically
   - C. by how much they are worth
   - D. in the order they were discovered

2. Which is the correct symbol for the element *silicon*?
   - A. SI
   - B. S
   - (C) Si
   - D. Sil

3. All atoms of an element are _____.
   - A. flammable
   - B. visible under a microscope
   - (C) alike
   - D. different

4. Elements that are usually shiny and good conductors of heat and electricity are known as _____.
   - A. gases
   - (B) metals
   - C. solids
   - D. nonmetals

5. The most recent model of an atom is the _____.
   - A. Bohr model
   - B. Plum Pudding model
   - C. Cookie Dough model
   - (D) Electron Cloud model

Unit Assessment Answer Key
Chemistry

6. Elements that are usually dull, brittle, and do not conduct electricity are known as
   A. gases
   B. metals
   C. solids
   Ⓓ nonmetals

7. Elements join together to form
   Ⓐ compounds
   B. ions
   C. protons
   D. atomic masses

8. Which picture best shows an atom?

A.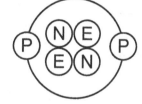

C.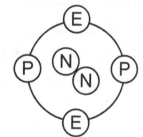

Ⓑ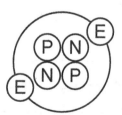

D.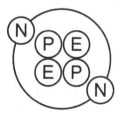

9. In order for a chemical reaction to take place, a certain amount of _____ must be present.
   A. heat
   B. friction
   C. chemicals
   Ⓓ energy

Unit Assessment Answer Key
Chemistry

10. Enzymes are _____ in the body that speed up chemical reactions.
(A) catalysts
B. cells
C. concentrations
D. chloroplasts

Answer the questions below by writing *protons, neutrons,* or *electrons* on the line or lines. (1 point each word)

11. The three main parts of an atom are _____**protons**_____, _____**electrons**_____, and _____**neutrons**_____.

12. An electrically neutral atom has the same number of _____**protons**_____ and _____**electrons**_____.

13. Particles with negative charges are called _____**electrons**_____.
Positively charged particles are called _____**protons**_____.
Particles with no charge are called _____**neutrons**_____.

14. To find the number of neutrons in an atom, you subtract the number of __**protons**__ from the mass number.

15. Fill in the chart with the correct name, symbol, or number.
(12 points: 1 for each item)

Element	Symbol	Atomic Number	Atomic Mass Rounded	Electrons	Protons	Neutrons
Calcium	Ca	20	40	20	20	20
Boron	B	5	11	5	5	6

Unit Assessment Answer Key
Chemistry

Tell which element is in each compound and the number of atoms of that element. (2 points each)

16. NaCl ___**sodium (1), chlorine (1)**___

17. $CoCl_2$ ___**cobalt (1), chlorine (2)**___

18. H_2SO_4 ___**hydrogen (2), sulfur (1), oxygen (4)**___

Write the formula for the compound described. (3 points each)

19. 1 atom of carbon, 2 atoms of oxygen ___**CO_2**___

20. 1 atom of copper, 1 atom of sulfur, 4 atoms of oxygen ___**$CuSO_4$**___

21. 2 atoms of aluminum, 3 atoms of sulfur ___**Al_2S_3**___

22. Give an example of how two elements changed properties when they formed a compound. (2 points) _____
Answers may include the fact that iron acetate and ammonia form a green blob and highly flammable sodium and chlorine gas form table salt, which is safe to eat.

Tell if the following solutions are acidic or basic.
23. pH = 12 ___**basic**___
24. pH = 3 ___**acidic**___

25. Write the equation that matches the description. (2 points)
One atom of zinc reacts with one atom of sulfur to yield one molecule of zinc sulfide. ___**$Zn + S \longrightarrow ZnS$**___

Unit Assessment Answer Key
Chemistry

26. Adding a catalyst and increasing the concentration of a reactant are two ways of speeding up a chemical reaction. Describe two more ways. (2 points) _____

Increasing the temperature and increasing the surface area of a reactant will speed up a chemical reaction.

_____

27. What clues should you look for to tell you that a chemical reaction has occurred? (2 points) _____

a color change, temperature change, the formation of bubbles, or the formation of a new solid

28. Describe how iodine can tell you if there is starch in a substance. (2 points) _____

Iodine turns from yellowish-brown to deep purple-black in the presence of starch. If iodine comes into contact with starch, it will change to this color.

29. Most organic compounds are made of just four elements. What are they? (1 point for each element)

carbon, oxygen, hydrogen, nitrogen

Learning Coach Guide
Lesson 1: The Cell Theory

Compared to most scientific discoveries, ideas about cells began forming not that long ago. In the 1600s, people began wondering about what makes up living things. We now know that the smallest part of any living thing is a cell--with organelles that perform jobs much like the organs in your body. Learn the parts of plant and animal cells and their jobs.

As recently as the 1800s, scientists were able to answer many questions about cells by using better microscopes and data from earlier research. Learn the three ideas of the cell theory and the basic parts of all cells. Complete a time line of cell-related events.

Lesson Objectives

- Identify the major structures of the cell (such as cell membrane, cytoplasm, and nucleus) and describe their functions.
- Describe the three major ideas of the cell theory.

PREPARE

Approximate lesson time is 60 minutes.

Materials

For the Student
- Did You Know?

For the Adult
- Did You Know? Answer Key

Lesson Notes

When asked what we are "made of," people often assume they are talking about personality. In biology, however, the question is literal, and has an answer. We are made of cells. This is the first element in what is known as the *cell theory: All living things are made of cells.* A *theory* is a general scientific principle that has observable evidence to support it. The cell theory, then, is a generalization about living things based on many observations--in this case, that the living things so far encountered have been made of cells. The second element of the cell theory is: *The cell is the basic unit of structure and function in living things.* Your student may recall that the atom is the basic unit of all matter. If we understand how atoms work, we understand much about how bigger things work. In a similar way, to understand, say, a giraffe, it helps to understand what a giraffe is made of--cells.

The third element of the cell theory is: *Living cells come only from other living cells.* We live in a time when this statement may seem obvious. Where else would living things come from? But this was not always the case. At one time people thought that maggots came spontaneously from dead meat. This actually makes a kind of sense. If you watch a dead animal, sooner or later you will see maggots on it. It was not until 1668 that Italian physicist Francesco Redi showed that maggots hatched from tiny eggs laid by flies.

These ideas about cells have led to all sorts of insights. For example, if all cells come from other cells, then cells must have the ability to reproduce. How do they do that? A dog is made of thousands of cells but starts off as only one. So how do all the other cells come about? How do they each know what kind of cell to become? How does the whole collection of cells work together to make a dog?

All cells have two critical structures--a cell membrane and cytoplasm. The *cell membrane* is the outer material that surrounds the cell. It is composed of a double layer of molecules, with embedded structures that allow interactions between the inside and outside of the cell. The *cytoplasm* is the interior of the cell and contains different structures, depending on the kind of cell, that are used in the cell's life processes.

Plant and animal cells contain a nucleus. The *nucleus* is the "command center" of the cell, and holds genetic instructions that determine how the cell operates, what molecules it makes, and how it responds to signals. Cell structures are adapted to their roles. For example:

Nerve cells have membranes that carry electrical signals. Endocrine cells have structures that make, and secrete, hormones. Cells in the eyes have structures that change light energy into electrical signals. Plant cells are surrounded by cell walls that support and protect them.

Keywords and Pronunciation

Anton van Leeuwenhoek (AHN-tohn vahn LAY-ven-hook)

cell : The basic unit of life, of which all living things are made. Some organisms are made up of only one cell.

cell membrane : The flexible, double-layered covering of all cells. The cell membrane is composed of a double layer of molecules.

chloroplast (KLOR-uh-plast) : The "solar panel" of plant cells, in which energy from the sun is converted into stored chemical energy by the process of photosynthesis. Chloroplasts contain chlorophyll and are found in plant cells, but not in animal cells.

cytoplasm (SIY-tuh-pla-zuhm) : The jelly-like matter of a living cell that is outside the nucleus. Organelles are contained in cytoplasm.

endocrine (EN-duh-kruhn)

Francesco Redi (frahn-CHAYS-koh REHD-ee)

Matthias Schleiden (mah-TEE-uhs SHLIY-duhn)

nucleus (NOO-klee-uhs) : The command center of plant and animal cells, which contains the information needed to direct activities for building, maintaining and operating the cell. Information in the nucleus determines which molecules the cell makes.

prokaryotes (proh-KAIR-ee-ohts)

Rudolf Virchow (ROO-dawlf FIHR-koh)

TEACH
Activity 1: What Are You Made Of? *(Online)*

Instructions
Have your student read through the Explore on her own. Reinforce and explain difficult concepts as needed.

Explore Suggestions:
Check your student's understanding by asking the following questions:
1. To make any statements about cells, what did scientists have to do a lot of? (observing and testing)
2. Are cells living? (yes)
3. Would you find cells in a computer or in a tire? Why not? (No, because they are not living.)

Screen 5: What is the largest cell you've ever seen? (eggs are cells!)

After this activity, check to see if your student can do the following:
- Identify the major structures of the cell (such as cell membrane, cytoplasm, and nucleus) and describe their functions.
- Describe the three major ideas of the cell theory.

If your student has difficulty with any of these concepts, you may wish to review the Explore with her and have her explain the key points on each screen.

Activity 2: Did You Know? (Online)
Instructions
Teaching:

Ideas about cells have been around for a long time. As your student moves through the activity, point out how scientists were able to build upon each other's work. Better microscopes led to better observations and more detailed theories.

What to Expect:

Your student should be able to describe events related to the development of the cell theory, the three ideas of the cell theory, and three basic parts of cells: cell membrane, cytoplasm, and nucleus.

Answers:

See Answer Key.

ASSESS

Lesson Assessment: The Cell Theory (*Online*)

Students will complete an offline assessment based on the lesson objectives. Print the assessment and have students complete it on their own. Use the answer key to score the assessment, and then enter the results online. The attached answer key is the most current and may not coincide with previously printed guides.

Name _____   Date _____

Did You Know? Answer Key

Did you know major cell discoveries have been taking place for hundreds of years? But that's not all! Use the lesson and the links in Lesson Resources to answer the questions and learn lesser-known facts about the development of the cell theory.

1. Did you know people once thought living things could come from nonliving things? What scientist proved this idea wrong by experimenting with rotting meat? **Francesco Redi**

2. Did you know the first person to observe cells through a microscope thought they looked like tiny rooms? Who observed these cells? **Robert Hooke**

3. Did you know the inventor of the simple microscope kept how he made it a secret until he died? What is a simple microscope? Who invented it? **A simple microscope is a microscope that uses only one lens for magnification. It was invented by Anton van Leeuwenhoek.**

4. Did you know that scientists once thought the "dark spot" in cells wasn't important? Name the Scottish botanist who paid attention to this spot and named it "nucleus." **Robert Brown**

5. Did you know that the botanist who stated that plants are made of cells started his career as a lawyer? Who was that lawyer-turned-botanist? **Mathias Schleiden**

6. Did you know that it took longer to figure out that animals are also made of cells? Name the botanist who proposed this idea. **Theodor Schwann**

Did You Know? Answer Key

7. Do you know the first two statements of the cell theory?
Write them here:

 a. **All living things are made of cells.**
 _____

 b. **The cell is the basic unit of structure and function in**
 living things.
 _____

8. Did you know the scientist who developed the third part of the cell
theory was once challenged to a duel... of sausages? Who was this
scientist? **Rudolph Virchow**
_____

9. What is the third statement of the cell theory?
 c. **All cells come from other living cells.**
 _____

Did You Know? Answer Key

Cell Diagram
Draw a diagram of a cell that includes a nucleus, membrane, and cytoplasm.

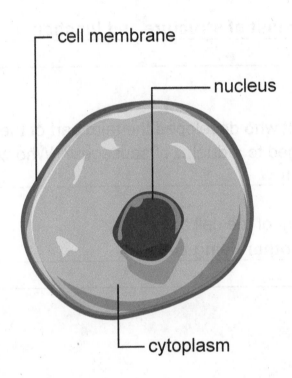

cell membrane

nucleus

cytoplasm

Name _____   Date _____

Lesson Assessment Answer Key

Fill in the blanks to complete the cell theory.

1. All _____**living things**_____ are made of cells.
2. The _____**cell**_____ is the basic unit of structure and function in living things.
3. Living cells come only from _____**other living cells**_____.

4. Draw a cell with a nucleus, cytoplasm, and cell membrane.

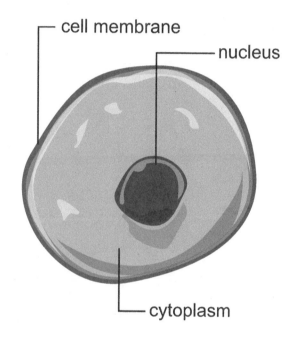

cell membrane

nucleus

cytoplasm

A *simile* compares one thing to something else that functions in a similar way. For example, you might say a person who works very hard for a long time is "like a machine." What is a cell like? How about its parts? Choose something to compare a cell and its parts to and explain why you made those choices.

5. A cell is like... ___**any object that carries out many**___
   ___**functions or makes up a larger whole (bricks in a wall).**___

Lesson Assessment Answer Key

6. A nucleus is like… **any object that controls activities (director, brain).**

7. Cytoplasm is like… **any substance that holds other parts, not necessarily jelly-like (fruit beneath the skin, pasta sauce with vegetables).**

8. A cell membrane is like… **any type of boundary (wall or skin of a fruit).**

Learning Coach Guide
Lesson 2: Cell Organelles

A cell contains parts called *organelles,* which are responsible for carrying out the cell's life processes. Study the names and functions of cell organelles. Make a model cell using foods such as gelatin and fruits.

Lesson Objectives

- Recognize the major cell organelles (for example, endoplasmic reticulum, ribosomes, Golgi bodies, chloroplasts, chromosomes, mitochondria, and vacuoles) and describe their functions.
- Distinguish between plant and animal cells.

PREPARE

Approximate lesson time is 60 minutes.

Advance Preparation

- You will need certain foods to make a cell model. These foods are prunes, mandarin oranges, grapes, a carrot, raisins, a tortilla, and a banana.
- Before the lesson, shred the carrot. Cut the shreds so they are small. Tear strips of tortilla and slice thin pieces of banana.

Materials

For the Student

    🖳 This Is Your Life, Cell!

    🖳 A Cell You Can Eat

    bag, clear plastic (2)

    food - carrot shreds

    food - green grapes

    food - Mandarin oranges

    food - prunes

    food - raisins

    pot with lid

    twist tie (2)

    bowl - large mixing

    gelatin - yellow

    spoon

    water - boiling

For the Adult

    🖳 This Is Your Life, Cell! Answer Key

    🖳 A Cell You Can Eat Answer Key

Lesson Notes

Just as the body has organs inside it to do the work of maintaining life--digesting food, respiration, pumping blood--so do individual cells have *organelles* inside them to perform the cell's functions.

All cells have a cell membrane and cytoplasm.

The *cell membrane* is the cell's boundary. The *cytoplasm* is the material in which the organelles are located. The cell membrane keeps the cytoplasm inside the cell and helps the cell maintain its shape. The membrane controls what goes into and comes out of the cell. It lets in, and keeps in, useful things, while sending out and keeping out non-useful or harmful material.

Both plant and animal cells have a *nucleus*, which directs the cell's activities. The nucleus is completely inside the cell and contains the information on how the cell is made, what its functions are, and how to execute those functions. This information, which makes up the instructions for the cell, is in the chromosomes.

Chromosomes are long molecules of DNA, somewhat like strings of letters that spell out messages. Primarily, these messages tell the cell how to build large molecules called *proteins*. Proteins are building blocks for the cell and also help it function.

To build proteins, the chromosomes' information is sent out to the cytoplasm using molecules of RNA. The RNA goes to the *ribosomes*--tiny round "factories" where the protein is put together according to the instructions from the chromosomes.

Some ribosomes are in the *endoplasmic reticulum*, or ER--a network of membranes inside the cell. Molecules important to the cell, including proteins, are made in the ER. The ER may store some of the molecules made there. It can also move them to other places in the cell or to the plasma membrane.

Finally, molecules may be sent from the ER to the Golgi body. The *Golgi body* puts the molecules in packages to go to other places in the cell.

The *chloroplast* is the structure green plants use to change sunlight into usable chemical energy. Only plant cells have chloroplasts.

Another energy handler in both plant and animal cells is the mitochondrion. *Mitochondria* are organelles in which chemical energy is changed into a form that the cell can use.

Vacuoles are like special containers surrounded by a membrane. They can be used for bringing in, storing, and digesting food, storing and expelling waste, storing other molecules, or pumping extra water out.

In plant cells, a *cell wall* is a stiff structure outside the cell membrane that gives the cell its shape and strength. Animal cells do not have cell walls.

All cells have chromosomes. In both plant and animal cells the chromosomes are in a nucleus surrounded by a membrane.

Both plant and animal cells also have:

- Endoplasmic reticulum
- Golgi bodies
- Mitochondria
- Vacuoles

Plant cells have cell walls and chloroplasts, but animal cells don't.

As a general observation, particular types of cells have different jobs they specialize in, and different ways to do them, with variations in how they're structured.

Keywords and Pronunciation

cell wall : The stiff structure outside the cell membrane in a plant cell that provides support for the cell. Animal cells do not have cell walls.

chloroplast (KLOR-uh-plast) : The "solar panel" of plant cells, in which energy from the sun is converted into stored chemical energy by the process of photosynthesis. Chloroplasts contain chlorophyll and are found in plant cells, but not in animal cells.

chromosomes (KROH-muh-sohms) : Thread-like structures containing protein and made of DNA, which itself contains the instructions for building, maintaining, and operating the cell.

cytoplasm (SIY-tuh-pla-zuhm) : The jelly-like matter of a living cell that is outside the nucleus. Organelles are contained in cytoplasm.

endoplasmic reticulum (EN-doh-plaz-mihk rih-TIHK-kyuh-luhm) : An organelle that makes, stores, and transports molecules in the cell. Ribosomes are found in some parts of the endoplasmic reticulum.

Golgi (GOHL-jee)

Golgi bodies (GOHL-jee) : Organelles that package molecules to send elsewhere within a cell. Golgi bodies are named for Camillo Golgi, who first described the structures in 1898.

mitochondria (miy-tuh-KAHN-dree-uh) : "Power plants" in the cytoplasm, where energy is released to a usable form, for organisms to function. The singular is mitochondrion. Mitochondria are dense in muscle cells, which need plenty of energy to contract.

organelle (or-guh-NEL) : A differentiated structure within a cell--such as a mitochondrion, vacuole, or chloroplast--that performs a specific function. A mitochondrion is an organelle that changes chemical energy into a form that the cell can use.

ribosomes (RIY-buh-sohmz) : Organelles that produce protein for the cell. Ribosomes build proteins according to instructions from chromosomes.

vacuoles (VA-kyuh-wohls) : Organelles that store food, water, and wastes in a cell and help get rid of wastes. In a plant cell, a large central vacuole takes up most of the cell.

TEACH
Activity 1: Inside a Cell (Online)
Instructions
Have your student read through the Explore on her own. Reinforce and explain difficult concepts as needed.

Explore Suggestions:

In Lesson 1, The Cell Theory, your student made a basic drawing of a cell with a membrane, cytoplasm, and nucleus. Have her add to that drawing as she reads through the content in this activity.

After this activity, check to see if your student can do the following:

- Recognize the major cell organelles (for example, endoplasmic reticulum, ribosomes, Golgi bodies, chloroplasts, chromosomes, mitochondria, and vacuoles) and describe their functions.
- Distinguish between plant and animal cells.

If your student has difficulty with any of these concepts, you may wish to review the Explore with her and have her explain the key points on each screen.

Activity 2: This Is Your Life, Cell! *(Offline)*

Instructions

Teaching:

Cell activities are carried out by parts called *organelles*. Your student will read descriptions of organelles and be asked to identify them. She may refer to the Explore if she needs help.

What to Expect:

Your student should be able to complete the activity on her own by referring to the content in the Explore. She should recognize major cell organelles and understand the difference between plant and animal cells.

Answers:

See Answer Key.

Activity 3: A Cell You Can Eat *(Offline)*

Instructions

Teaching:

Plant and animal cells have many parts in common, called *organelles.* Additionally, plant cells have cell walls and chloroplasts. Your student will make a gelatin model of a cell using different fruits to represent parts. Allow your student to refer to the content in the Explore to fill out the organelle chart.

What to Expect:

When the gelatin sets, you will have a cell that your student can eat. Your student should be able to describe cell organelles by name and be familiar with functions of major cell organelles, such as the nucleus, cytoplasm, cell wall, cell membrane, chromosomes, mitochondria, and chloroplasts.

Answers:

See Answer Key.

Safety

This lesson involves eating or working with food. Before beginning, check with your doctor, if necessary, to find out whether your student will have any allergic reaction to the food.

ASSESS

Lesson Assessment: Cell Organelles *(Online)*

Students will complete an offline assessment based on the lesson objectives. Print the assessment and have students complete it on their own. Use the answer key to score the assessment, and then enter the results online. The attached answer key is the most current and may not coincide with previously printed guides.

TEACH
Activity 4: Visit a Virtual Cell *(Online)*
Instructions

Teaching:

Allow your student to explore the virtual cell on her own. She may select an organelle, then cut it and rotate it for different views.

Troubleshooting:

Arrows to the left of the image provide navigation forward and back through the site.

What to Expect:

Your student will view another model of cells and cell organelles.

Name _____   Date _____

A Cell You Can Eat Answer Key

Why do scientists make models? Models help us study things we can't easily see.

You can make a model of a cell using different fruits to represent different organelles. Study the chart. Fill in either the name of the cell organelle or its description. When you finish, make a cell you can eat!

Fruit	Cell Organelle	Description
Prune	**Nucleus**	Command center, directs cell activities
Gelatin	Cytoplasm	**Contains the cell's organelles**
Mandarin oranges	**Mitochondria**	Change chemical energy to a form that is usable by the cell
Green grapes	Chloroplasts	**In plants, change sunlight into chemical energy**
Carrot shreds	**Chromosomes**	Contains the genetic information for the cell in its DNA
Raisins	Ribosome	**Tiny round "factories" where the protein is put together according to the instructions from some chromosome**
Thin pieces of tortilla, stacked and crumpled	**Endoplasmic reticulum**	A maze-like network of membranes that store or move molecules in the cell
Thin slices of banana, stacked	**Golgi body**	Packages molecules to send to other places in the cell
Bag	Cell membrane	**Acts as a skin for the cell and controls what goes in and out**
Cup	**Cell wall**	Rigid, gives plant cells their shape

Name _____   Date _____

A Cell You Can Eat Answer Key

Make the Model

Materials

2 plastic sandwich bags
twist ties
boiling water
large mixing bowls
spoons
prune
gelatin, yellow
Mandarin oranges
green grapes

carrot shreds
raisins
thin strips of tortilla, folded
thin slices of banana, stacked
cup (8 oz)
water
heat source
pot

Procedure

1. Leave one plastic bag open. This represents the cell membrane of an animal cell.
2. Place the second bag into the cup, completely lining the cup with a little extra sticking out from the top. This represents the cell membrane and cell wall of a plant cell.
3. Make gelatin following the directions on the packet.
4. Place the cell bag close to full with warm gelatin. This represents the cytoplasm.
5. Place the cell "organelles" into the bag: a prune to represent a nucleus with a few carrot shred chromosomes stuck inside, mandarin oranges for mitochondria, several bananna slices stacked together for a golgi body, folded tortilla strips for endoplasmic reticulum, and raisins for ribosomes. Place a few "ribosomes" between the layers of "endoplasmic reticulum."
6. Close the "cell" using the twist tie.
7. Repeat steps 5 and 6 for the plant cell, adding grapes for chloroplasts.
8. Put them in the refrigerator to set.

Name _____ Date _____

A Cell You Can Eat Answer Key

Questions

1. What parts do plant and animal cells have in common? List all of them, not just those used in the model. __nucleus, cell membrane,__ __chromosomes, mitochondria, endoplasmic reticulum, Golgi__ __bodies, vacuoles, cytoplasm__

2. What parts are different between plant and animal cells? How does this affect what the cells do? __Plant cells have chloroplasts and__ __a cell wall, but animal cells do not. Chloroplasts allow plants__ __to convert the sun's energy into food. Cell walls support the__ __structure of a plant, but limit movement__

3. If you were looking at cells with a microscope, how would you know whether they came from a plant or an animal? __A plant cell will have__ __chloroplasts and a cell wall and a large central vacuole. An__ __animal cell will not.__

4. What types of cells have chloroplasts? What function do chloroplasts serve? __Plant cells have chloroplasts. Chloroplasts convert the__ __sun's energy into a form that is useful to the cell.__

5. What information do chromosomes carry? __genetic instructions,__ __including instructions for making proteins__

Name _____ Date _____

This Is Your Life, Cell! Answer Key

Read the script from This is Your Life, Cell! Fill in the blanks with the names of cell organelles. Use the Word Bank to help you.

Word Bank

Nucleus	Cell Membrane	Mitochondria
Cell Wall	Golgi Body	Vacuole
Chloroplasts	Ribosomes	Cytoplasm
Chromosomes	Endoplasmic Reticulum	

(Lights on, crowd cheers)

BART FRANKLIN, HOST: Welcome, kids, to "This is Your Life" --a show that's guaranteed to bring a smile to your face and a tear to your eye. I'm Bart Franklin, your always-smiling, always-talking host. Today our guest is Cell—a small little guy, but alive and kicking nonetheless. Cell is here to be reunited with his old friends, the organelles. How are you feeling, Cell?

CELL *(in a young voice):* Well, Bart, I can't believe I am here. I am so happy, I could split!

BART: Woah! That's pretty serious, kids! Do you know what happens when cells divide? More cells. We had better get this show started before we've got more than we can handle. But first, let's see whom Cell's brought to the show. Cell?

CELL: Bart, I've brought some of my good friends today-- there's Muscle Cell and Nerve Cell. I also brought Red Blood Cell, but he doesn't talk much on account of the fact that he doesn't have a nucleus.

BART: Well, that is a shame, Cell. Speaking of nucleus, would you believe we've got your pal Nucleus right here in the studio tonight?

This Is Your Life, Cell! Answer Key

CELL: No! Not old Nucleus!

BART: It's true. Now, before we've got double trouble on our hands, how about we begin?

CELL: Sure thing, Bart!

BART: Okay, Cell. Listen to this first mystery guest.

GUEST 1 *(in a rubbery, shaky voice):* Hi ya, Cell. I'm the guy that holds it all together for ya. I hold your nucleus, your chloroplasts, even your endoplasmic reticulum. I'm kinda jelly-like. Once, I helped you stretch out and sorta change shape because I give ya your shape. Do you remember me?

CELL *(thinking):* Hmmm… Jelly-like? Holds all my organelles? You must be _____**Cytoplasm**_____ !

BART: Excellent work. *(crowd claps)* Let's hear from mystery guest number two.

GUEST 2 *(in a hurried voice):* Oh, Cell, Cell, I could hardly come today--I was so busy changing chemical energy into something you can use. I am always changing energy, like changing a check into money at the bank. Tell me quickly who I am so I can get back to work.

CELL *(excited):* Oh, I remember you! You were always a powerhouse! You're _____**Mitochondria**_____!

BART: Two for two! *(crowd claps)* Okay, Cell, see if you can figure out this third mystery guest…

This Is Your Life, Cell! Answer Key

GUEST 3 *(in an intelligent voice):* Ah, yes, Cell. Long time, no diffusion. Well, in order for you to do your job, you need me to give you instructions. I have all of the genetic information in me inside a long molecule called DNA. Just who might I be?

CELL: Is that you, Nucleus?

BART: Oooooh, Cell, not this time. *(crowd gasps)* But I hang out with Nucleus. Try again. Think DNA and genetic information.

CELL *(with a smile):* It can't be…I thought you'd been copied long ago. Is it _____**Chromosomes**_____?

BART: Thatta boy, Cell! *(crowd claps)* Be sure to save a hug for your old pal. *(crowd sighs)* Okay, Cell. Now things are going to get a little tough. We've got two organelles here this time because they are often found together. Listen closely to the next mystery guests!

GUEST 4 *(a tiny voice):* Cell, it is so good to see you. Just backstage I was talking to Chromosomes and we were remembering how I used to follow their instructions to put together proteins. You often find me in the folds of the next mystery guest.

GUEST 5 *(a deep voice from offstage):* Cell…some have described my looks as a maze, but you can't get lost in me. I let my buddy here stay within my membrane network. I also store and move molecules. I hope you know who I am, Cell, because it's been a long time and I sure miss ya.

CELL: Wow, this is a tough one, Bart. There's only one maze-like network I know that lets molecules in and out. It's __**Endoplasmic Reticulum**__. And that fourth guest that can be found there… that must be _____**Ribosomes**_____!

This Is Your Life, Cell! Answer Key

BART: Excellent job, Cell! Just look at the crowd cheering! *(clapping)* Since you did so well with two organelles last time, let's try that again. Plus, we're running out of time and we've got to show some commercials before our next guest, Mr. Zinc. He's getting quite unstable backstage. Let's hear from our next two mystery guests.

GUEST 6 *(a kind voice):* Cell! The flight here was terrible! I felt sick, but no one could tell because I am already green. Remember all those times you were hungry? I was able to take the sun's energy and change it into chemical energy so you were fed. It was not an easy job, but I was happy to do it for you all these years.

GUEST 7 *(a tough voice):* Cell, I've got some bumps and bruises and my back hurts from holding you up so rigidly for so long. I gave you your shape, remember? My feet hurt a little, too. Many times I thought about quitting, but I am loyal to you, Cell.

CELL *(about to cry):* Bart, I'd know those two anywhere. They are the reason I am a plant cell. Come on out here, __**Chloroplasts**__ and _____**Cell Wall**_____!

BART: Aw, gee folks, isn't that sweet? Cell, we just got great news. One of your organelles was not able to make it today, but we've got her on the phone. Listen in carefully to this guest!

GUEST 8 *(a military voice):* Hello there, Cell! Hold on a second there--*(away from the phone)* hey molecules--get over here, please! It's time to package you up and send you to other areas. Quit moving around now, you've got a job to do! *(back on phone)* I'm sorry, Cell, there's a lot to do around here. Do you know who I am?

CELL: Is that you, Vacuole?

This Is Your Life, Cell! Answer Key

GUEST 8: Do I sound like a liquid bubble? I do a hard job for you Cell, packaging up molecules and sending them on their way. Try again!

CELL: Could it be you, _____**Golgi Body**_____?

BART: Cell! You've done it again. *(crowd cheers)* Okay, just two more to go. Next guest!

GUEST 9 *(with a British accent):* Hallo there, Cell! It's me, back here directing everyone else. Mitochondria, I do wish you would stay still. Goodness chromosomes, what *are* you doing? Very well. Cell, you know me. I direct all of your activities, like a command center inside you.

CELL: It's _____**Nucleus**_____! How are you? Don't work too hard back there!

BART: He's done it again! Okay, Cell, we've got one more organelle here to see you today. Let's listen in and see if you can identify this last mystery guest.

GUEST 10 *(a motherly voice):* Oh Cell, Cell, Cell…without me, you'd have no shape. I protect you like a skin. I am the outermost layer of you, next to the wall. Remember when we looked like a rectangle, then sort of like a rounded rectangle? That was Cytoplasm and me! I also let things pass into and out of you. Do you remember me?

CELL *(in tears)*: Could it be? I know that voice anywhere… Is that you, _____**Cell Membrane**_____?

BART: You've done it! *(crowd cheers and claps)* Excellent, Cell. In just a moment we'll reunite you with all your cell organelles-- except Golgi Body, of course. She wishes she could have been here today.

This Is Your Life, Cell! Answer Key

CELL: I can hardly wait.

BART: That's great, Cell. Before we go, have you got anything you'd like to say?

CELL: This has been amazing, Bart. When do I get to take my trip to Hawaii?

BART: Well, this isn't that kind of show, Cell. But we *can* reunite you with your organelles-- how about it, folks?

CELL: But I'd rather go to Hawaii!

BART: Cell, you'e kind of rooted here. You live in an evergreen tree. I just don't think Hawaii is possible. But we have some nice parting gifts, including the board game version of "This is Your Life!" How about we get all your organelles out here for a great big hug--come on, gang! We need to cut to a commercial, be right back!

CELL: But I learned to hula!

(lights go down)

Name _____ Date _____

Lesson Assessment Answer Key

Choose the best answer.

1. Which organelle changes chemical energy into a form that is usable by the cell?
   (A) mitochondria
   B. ribosome
   C. nucleus
   D. cell wall

2. Which organelle holds genetic information in the molecule DNA?
   A. vacuole
   B. cell membrane
   (C) chromosome
   D. Golgi body

3. Which tiny, round "factory" puts together protein and is often found in the endoplasmic reticulum?
   A. chromosome
   B. chloroplast
   C. Golgi body
   (D) ribosome

4. Which organelle is responsible for packaging molecules to send to other places in the cell?
   A. mitochondria
   B. vacuole
   (C) Golgi body
   D. nucleus

5. Which organelle appears to be empty but is filled with liquid?
   A. cell membrane
   B. chloroplast
   (C) vacuole
   D. ribosome

Lesson Assessment Answer Key

6. Study the illustration. Which cell is likely to come from a plant?

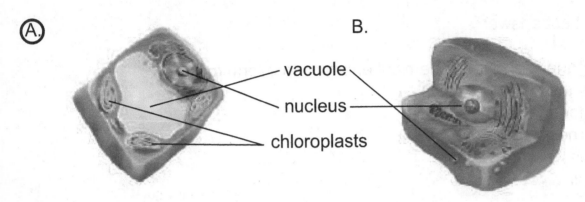

Ⓐ

B.

vacuole

nucleus

chloroplasts

7. How is a cell membrane different from a cell wall? _____
   A cell wall is rigid and gives a plant cell its shape. A
   cell membrane acts like a skin and is not rigid. A cell
   membrane more selectively controls what goes in and
   out of the cell.

8. What parts are different between plant and animal cells? How
   does this affect what the cells can do? _____
   Plant cells have chloroplasts and a cell wall, but animal
   cells do not. Chloroplasts allow plants to convert the sun's
   energy into food. Cell walls support the structure of a plant,
   but limit movement.

Learning Coach Guide
Lesson 3: Diffusion, Osmosis, and Active Transport

For a cell to carry out its normal processes, it must be able to move molecules in and out through its cell membrane. This enables cells to be fed, pass nerve signals, and secrete hormones when needed. Explore diffusion, osmosis, and active transport--three ways cells are able to get particles in and out through their cell membranes. Make models to observe diffusion through a plastic "membrane" and osmosis through an egg.

Lesson Objectives

- Recognize various ways in which molecules are transported across the cell membrane.
- Define *diffusion* as the process by which molecules move from areas of higher concentration to areas of lower concentration.
- Recognize that water moves through membranes by *osmosis*--diffusion of water through a semipermeable membrane.

PREPARE

Approximate lesson time is 60 minutes.

Advance Preparation

- The model cells you make in this lesson will need to stand overnight. You may start the lesson and come back to it the next day or prepare this activity ahead of time. Print the Diffusion Through a Membrane activity sheet for directions.
- Follow the directions in the Osmosis activity sheet to soak an egg in vinegar for at least two days. If, after two days, the shell is not completely dissolved or softened, leave the egg in vinegar an extra day.

Materials

For the Student

📖 Diffusion Through a Membrane

    bag, clear plastic - sandwich bags-no zipper

    cornstarch - 5 mL (1 tsp)

    drinking glass - 355 mL (12oz) (2)

    iodine

    measuring spoon - teaspoon

    rock - small

    eyedropper

    graduated cylinder

    measuring cup

    spoon - mixing

    string - 30 cm (2)

    water

📖 Osmosis

    food - corn syrup

    food - one raw egg

    household item - clear 500 mL containers (2)

    vinegar - 250 mL

    graduated cylinder - 250 mL

    spoon

    tape - masking

For the Adult

    📖 Diffusion Through a Membrane Answer Key

    📖 Osmosis Answer Key

Lesson Notes

Cells need to have molecules move around inside them as well as moving in or out altogether. The cell must be able to take food in and send waste out. In the case of nerve cells, they must be able to take in and send out charged particles quickly every time a signal passes along the cell. And cells that produce hormones must be able to excrete the hormones into the bloodstream at the right time.

Three major ways by which molecules move inside cells, or into and out of cells, are: (a) Diffusion; (b) Osmosis; (c) Active transport. The first two of these options are *passive*, meaning they occur without the cell using any energy. The third is *active*, and requires energy. One can loosely think of passive molecular motion as happening "without the cell needing to do anything" and active molecular motion as "requiring the cell to do something about it."

Diffusion is the tendency of molecules in a liquid or gas to spread out from areas of high concentration into areas of lower concentration. Diffusion can be observed any time someone squirts a perfume bottle in one room and people in another room smell the fragrance. The molecules of perfume did not stay in a concentrated cloud around the place where they were sprayed. Rather, they quickly spread out to areas of lower concentration. The scent diffused through the house.

Any barrier or membrane that lets molecules through it is said to be *permeable* to those molecules. A membrane that lets through some things and not others is *semipermeable*.

One could have, for example, a membrane that has microscopic holes too small for sugar to pass through but large enough for water to pass through. A teabag allows molecules of tea through, along with molecules of water, but blocks the large pieces of tea. Diffusion of water through a semipermeable membrane is called *osmosis.*

Cells cannot rely entirely on the passive motion of molecules. They need also to be able to move molecules into areas of higher concentration, opposite to the direction they would move by diffusion. This can be achieved with active transport. Moving molecules from a place of low to one of high concentration using both energy and carrier molecules in the membrane as help, is called *active transport.*

Another way cells move molecules in or out using energy is by using vacuoles. To get some things into the cell--such as food--the cell membrane surrounds the substance, "pinching it off" to make a vacuole with the substance inside. To get some things out, such as some waste, a vacuole containing the waste connects to the cell membrane and opens to the outside, releasing the contents. Similar processes move molecules around inside the cell as well.

Cell membranes are permeable to water, but less so to larger molecules. Pure or fresh water around cells tends to diffuse into them by osmosis. This makes cells in such water swell. The resulting pressure in plant cells, called *turgor pressure*, helps support the cell. Turgor pressure in plant cells explains why the leaves of a healthy plant stand up, while the leaves of a plant that has not been watered wilt and droop.

Keywords and Pronunciation

cell membrane : The flexible, double-layered covering of cells. Cell membranes help control what goes in and out of cells.

cytoplasm (SIY-tuh-pla-zuhm) : The jelly-like matter of a living cell that is outside the nucleus. Organelles are contained in cytoplasm.

diffusion : The process by which molecules tend to move from an area of higher concentration to an area of lower concentration. Diffusion of molecules from onions frying in the kitchen brings the smell to the living room.

osmosis (ahz-MOH-suhs) : the diffusion of water across a semipermeable membrane

permeable (PUHR-mee-uh-buhl) : Allowing molecules to pass or diffuse through. Any barrier or membrane that lets molecules through it is said to be permeable to those molecules.

semipermeable : Permeable to some molecules, but not to others. Cell membranes are semipermeable, permeable to water molecules, but not to larger molecules.

turgor (TUHR-guhr) : outward force on the cell wall of a plant that results from water contained within the cell; turgid pressure helps keep a plant rigid.

TEACH
Activity 1: Moving Through Membranes *(Online)*

Instructions

Have your student read through the Explore on her own. Reinforce and explain difficult concepts as needed.

Explore Suggestions:

Check your student's understanding by asking the following questions:

1. Describe the relationship between high and low concentrations in diffusion, osmosis, and active transport. (In diffusion and osmosis, molecules move from high concentration to low. In active transport, molecules move from low concentration to high.)

2. Have your student choose any or all of the three processes to describe or illustrate in her own words.

Screen 1: Teach your student the difference between *passive* and *active* by naming other passive and active processes. Discuss which require energy. Compare these to the processes of diffusion and osmosis (passive) and active transport (active). Examples: passive--sledding or skating downhill, leaves falling, a helium balloon rising; active--running, cooking, throwing a ball, an airplane taking off.

Screen 3: Review some chemistry concepts your student has learned. Have her recall the chemical formula for sugar ($C_6H_{12}O_6$) and for water (H_2O). Ask why the sugar molecules in the animation are so much larger than the water molecules. (There are many more atoms in a sugar molecule than a water molecule.)

Point out that osmosis is diffusion, but only of water molecules through a semipermeable membrane. Diffusion can be through a membrane or not, and can involve any kind of molecule that moves around.

After this activity, check to see if your student can:

- Define *diffusion* as the process by which molecules move from areas of high concentration to areas of low concentration.
- Recognize that water moves through membranes by *osmosis*--diffusion of water through a semipermeable membrane.
- Recognize various ways molecules are transported across the cell membrane.

If your student has difficulty with any of these concepts, you may wish to review the Explore with her and have her explain the key points on each screen.

Activity 2: Diffusion Through a Membrane *(Offline)*

Instructions

Teaching:

Explain that *diffusion* is the movement of molecules. Use the smell of popcorn as an example. Molecules will move from areas of high concentration (where the corn was popped) to areas of low concentration (other rooms or spaces nearby). Diffusion is different from osmosis in that osmosis involves only water going through a semipermeable membrane. Diffusion involves molecules in liquids and gases, and can occur through a membrane or, more simply, from one place to another with no membrane between. Your student will use a plastic bag as a model membrane to observe diffusion through a membrane.

What to Expect:

The iodine will be able to pass through the plastic bag and into the gelatin, turning a purple-black color when it comes in contact with starch. The molecules of iodine are small enough to pass through the holes in the bag. The molecules of iodine move from an area of high concentration outside the bag to an area of low concentration inside the bag. They also move around by diffusion inside the bag, away from the membrane where they entered, to fill the space inside.

Safety
Use caution when using a heat source and handling boiling water. Never leave your student unattended near boiling water.

Activity 3: Osmosis *(Offline)*
Instructions
Teaching:

Osmosis differs from diffusion in that it is concerned with the movement of water molecules through a semipermeable membrane. This type of membrane allows certain molecules to pass through, based on high and low concentrations. As in diffusion, in osmosis molecules move from areas of high concentration to areas of low concentration. Your student will observe osmosis in an experiment that uses a raw egg.

Troubleshooting:

Thick white syrup gives better results than thin syrup. If the eggshells have not completely dissolved after the end of two days, leave them an extra day. Handle the eggs carefully to avoid breaking the membranes.

What to Expect:

Your student should see a difference in the amount of liquid left in the containers due to osmosis. She should be able to explain that water molecules moved into and out of the cell membrane from areas of high concentration to areas of low concentration, and that this process is called *osmosis.*

ASSESS

Lesson Assessment: Diffusion, Osmosis, and Active Transport (*Online*)
Students will complete an online assessment based on the lesson objectives. The assessment will be scored by the computer. The attached answer key is the most current and may not coincide with previously printed guides.

Name _____   Date _____

Diffusion Through a Membrane Answer Key

Diffusion takes place when molecules in a gas or liquid spread out, moving from a place where they are highly concentrated to a place where they are not as concentrated. You experience the result of diffusion when smells from a kitchen reach you in a far-away room. Where is the area of high concentration of smelly molecules? ____**in the kitchen**____ Where is the area of low concentration of smelly molecules? _____
where they will reach you _____

Diffusion also happens in cells as molecules move in and out through the cell membrane. You can make a model to see how this works.

Materials
water
plastic sandwich bag (not the zipper-close type), 2
cornstarch
iodine
cup, 355 mL (12 oz.), 2
graduated cylinder
measuring spoon
measuring cup
small rock
marker

Procedure
1. Fill both bags with 5 mL cornstarch and 120 mL water.
2. Add a small rock about the size of a golf ball to each bag.
3. Knot the top of the bags to close them.
4. Fill the cups halfway with water.
5. Add 10 drops of iodine to one of the cups. Label this Cup 1. The cup of plain water will be Cup 2.
6. Place the bags in the cup. Completely submerge the bag of cornstarch mixture.

Diffusion Through a Membrane Answer Key

7. Wait 15 minutes, then make your observations. While waiting, answer the questions.

Questions

Think about concentrations. A more concentrated substance has more "stuff" in a given amount of it. A less concentrated substance has less "stuff."

1. In which is starch more concentrated—the bag or the cup?

   __**bag**__

2. For Cup 1: In which is iodine more concentrated—the bag or the cup? __**cup**__

	Starting Color	Color after 15 minutes
Solution in Cup 1	**Brown**	**Brown**
Bag in Cup 1	**White**	**Purple-black**
Solution in Cup 2	**Clear**	**Clear**
Bag in Cup 2	**White**	**White**

Analysis

You know that iodine changes to a deep purple-black when it comes into contact with starch. Use your observations to answer the questions.

1. Which substance moved, the iodine or the starch? **The iodine.**

2. How can you tell? **Iodine changes color when it is in contact with starch. The solution in the bag in Cup 1 turned a deep purple-black, which means that iodine moved into the bag. If cornstarch had moved out of the bag, the solution in the cup would have changed color.**

Diffusion Through a Membrane Answer Key

3. The plastic bag allowed which molecules to pass through—
water, cornstarch, or iodine? **_____iodine_____**

4. Diffusion happens when molecules move from areas of high
concentration to areas of low concentration. Which substance
diffused? **_____iodine_____**

5. What was the purpose of Cup 2? **to compare with Cup 1.**

6. Sketch Cup 1 and its bag below. Label the areas of high
concentration and low concentration at the start for both starch
and iodine. Use arrows to show how diffusion happened in this
investigation.

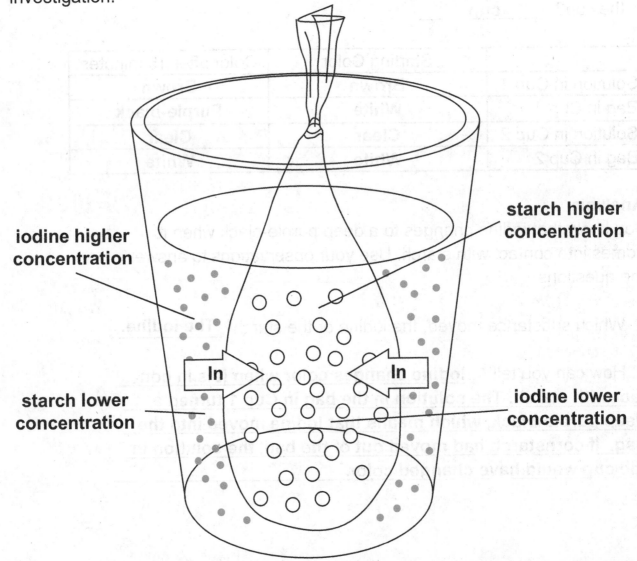

iodine higher concentration

starch higher concentration

starch lower concentration

iodine lower concentration

In   In

Diffusion Through a Membrane Answer Key

Conclusion

1. Explain how diffusion occurred in this investigation. Use your observations to write a detailed answer. **In this model, iodine diffused into a plastic bag containing starch. Iodine started more highly concentrated outside the bag, but moved to an area of lower concentration inside. Iodine changes color when it comes into contact with starch. Because the solution inside the bag turned to a deep purple-black, we know that the iodine diffused into the bag, rather than the starch diffusing out.**

2. What would happen if you did this experiment again, but placed iodine in the bag and the cornstarch solution in the cup? **The solution outside the bag would turn a deep purple-black.**

3. Tell why it is not a good idea to store iodine in a plastic bag. **Iodine molecules are small enough to seep through the plastic bag. The iodine will leak through the bag.**

Name _____   Date _____

Osmosis Answer Key

A membrane that is *semipermeable* will let some things through, but not others. If water molecules are able to pass from a high-concentration area to a low-concentration area through membranes like this, we call it *osmosis*.

A key fact to remember about osmosis is that it involves the movement of water molecules. Diffusion involves liquid and gas molecules, but when you are thinking about osmosis, think about water.

Use an egg to see how osmosis works.

Materials
one raw egg
two clear 500 mL containers
plates, 2
250 mL vinegar
250 mL corn syrup
water
spoon
masking tape
marker
graduated cylinder
measuring cups

Procedure:
1. Use the masking tape and marker to label the containers A and B.
2. Pour 250 mL of vinegar into container A. Mark the level of the vinegar with a piece of masking tape.
3. Pour 250 mL of syrup into container B. Compare the levels of the liquids in containers A and B to make sure they are the same. Mark the level of the syrup with a piece of masking tape.
4. Place the egg into container A. Make sure it is completely covered. Cover both containers with plates or other lids.
5. After two days, use the spoon to very carefully remove the egg from container A. Rinse the egg and place it into container B.
6. Mark the new level of the vinegar in container A with masking tape.

Name _____   Date _____

Osmosis Answer Key

7. Observe the egg the next day. Record its appearance in the Observations section on page 2.
8. Remove the egg and place it in water. Mark the new level of the syrup in container B with masking tape.

Observations

After two days in vinegar, what is the appearance of the egg? _____
The shell dissolves and the egg appears swollen.
_____

After another day in the syrup, what is the appearance of the egg? _____
The egg is soft and has shrunk.
_____

Was there more or less vinegar in container A after two days? **less** _____
Was there more or less syrup in container B after one day? **more** _____

Analysis

Follow directions *carefully* to answer the questions.

1. In container A, how can you tell that water from the vinegar moved into the egg? **The level of vinegar in the container was lower than when we started and we did not remove any vinegar from the contaner.**

2. In container B, how can you tell that water moved out of the egg?
The level of syrup in the container was higher than when we started, and we did not add any syrup to the container.

3. The egg has many molecules in its cytoplasm, some of which are water. Why did water move into the egg in container A? Tell about the concentrations of water molecules. **Water molecules are not highly concentrated inside the egg. They moved from an area of high concentration outside the egg to an area of low concentration inside the egg.**

Osmosis Answer Key

4. Why did water move out of the egg in container B? Tell about the concentrations of water molecules. __Water molecules moved__ __from an area of high concentration inside the egg to an area__ __of low concentration outside the egg.__

Conclusions

1. What part of the egg controlled what moved into and out of the egg? __the cell membrane__

2. What would happen if you left the egg you removed from the syrup in water? Explain your answer. __Water would move into__ __the egg. Water molecules inside the egg would have a lower__ __concentration than those outside the egg, so the water mol-__ __ecules would move inside.__

Learning Coach Guide
Lesson 4: Photosynthesis and Respiration

Investigate two cell processes--photosynthesis and respiration. *Photosynthesis* is the process by which plants use the sun's energy and carbon dioxide to make food and release oxygen. *Respiration* is a process by which most cells use oxygen and break down larger molecules to release energy in a usable form and carbon dioxide. The cycling of oxygen and carbon dioxide through these processes is important in maintaining balance in our life-sustaining system. Review these processes, then investigate gas exchange in common household plants.

Lesson Objectives

- Describe the process of *cellular respiration*.
- Describe the process of *photosynthesis* in plants.

PREPARE

Approximate lesson time is 60 minutes.

Advance Preparation

- Find a houseplant and a sunny location. Print Where are the Stomata? and follow the directions to set up the investigation. Coat the top sides of four leaves with a heavy layer of petroleum jelly. Coat the undersides of four other leaves with petroleum jelly. Place the plant in normal sunlight and water as usual for one week. Observe the plant during the lesson.
- You will need a sprig of elodea if you choose to do the Beyond the Lesson activity. You can buy elodea at a pet store or any other store that sells fish supplies.

Materials

For the Student

 📖 Yes, Teacher!

 📖 A Lot of Stomata

 petroleum jelly

 plant - with broad leaves

 knife - butter

 📖 Exhale!

 food - purple cabbage, head

 household item - drinking straw

 household item - heat source

 jar - pint size-with lids (3)

 plant - sprig of elodea

 aluminum foil

 bowl - mixing

 water

 water - distilled

For the Adult

 📖 Yes, Teacher! Answer Key

Lesson Notes

Almost all energy that organisms use has its origin in the sun. Plants use photosynthesis to turn energy in sunlight into chemical energy stored in food molecules they can later use. Animals that eat those plants, or that eat animals that ate those plants, take in the stored energy. Both animals and plants then use cellular respiration to release the energy to a form that they can easily use.

Photosynthesis is the process by which plants convert light energy into stored chemical energy.

Cellular respiration is the process by which both plants and animals convert their stored chemical energy into a form they can use easily and quickly.

Your student should not be confused by the term *respiration*, which is also used to mean *breathing*. *Cellular respiration*, specifically, refers to the shifting of chemical energy in cells, plant or animal, from a kind of storage molecule to a type of molecule in which the energy is easily available, like energy "cash." Breathing is related to cellular respiration in animals. It makes available to cells the oxygen necessary for cellular respiration, via the blood stream, and expels carbon dioxide, the waste product of cellular respiration.

The key to photosynthesis is *chlorophyll*, a large molecule in *chloroplasts*. Chlorophyll is also responsible for the green color of plants.

In photosynthesis, a plant uses carbon dioxide, water, and light energy to make glucose. Oxygen is released. To animals, however, and to plants that need to get the energy back out of the glucose, that same oxygen is essential. They use it in their own cellular respiration.

The glucose that results from photosynthesis has the captured light energy built into it, converted to chemical energy in a stable molecule. In other words, the plant has grabbed and stored energy that came from the sun.

Carbon Dioxide + Water + Light energy --> Glucose + Oxygen

From eating plants or other animals, animals get stored energy in glucose and other molecules they can break down into glucose. Both plants and animals can release their stored energy through cellular respiration. Respiration gets the energy to a form that cells can use easily--in the molecule ATP.

In the cytoplasm of cells, glucose is first broken down into smaller molecules. These molecules enter the mitochondria, where respiration breaks down the molecules, using oxygen and capturing the energy in ATP. Carbon dioxide is released and water is formed.

Now, energy that was stored in glucose is easily available to the cell in the ATP, the energy "cash" made in the mitochondria.

Your student should understand that photosynthesis and animal respiration are like opposites. The overall processes are nearly the reverse of each other. Photosynthesis uses energy from light to put together small molecules of carbon dioxide to make a larger molecule containing the energy, giving off oxygen in the process. Cellular respiration takes the larger molecule and, using oxygen, breaks the larger molecule down into smaller molecules of carbon dioxide, capturing the energy, in ATP. This can be expressed in chemical word equations.

Photosynthesis converts light energy into chemical energy in glucose, starting with carbon dioxide and water.

Light energy + Carbon Dioxide + Water --> Glucose + Oxygen

Respiration takes the chemical energy in glucose and, using oxygen, converts that energy to chemical energy the cell can use more easily, in ATP. It results in carbon dioxide and water.

Glucose + Oxygen --> Carbon Dioxide + Water + Energy in ATP

In this way photosynthesis in plants, and cellular respiration in both plants and animals, along with the molecules they use and create, are intimately linked to a great cycle of energy flow. This is why the well-being of animals and plants cannot be considered separately.

Keywords and Pronunciation

chlorophyll (KLOR-uh-fil) : A special, large molecule that "captures" light energy and starts its change into chemical energy in the process of photosynthesis. Chlorophyll gives many plants their green color.

chloroplasts (KLOR-uh-plasts) : Structures in green plant cells that enable plants to produce their own food by converting light energy into chemical energy in molecules of glucose. Animal cells do not have chloroplasts.

mitochondria (miy-tuh-KAHN-dree-uh) : "Power plants" in the cytoplasm, where energy is released to a usable form, for organisms to function. The singular is mitochondrion. Mitochondria are dense in muscle cells, which need plenty of energy to contract.

photosynthesis (foh-toh-SINT-thuh-suhs) : The process by which plant cells convert light energy from the sun into chemical energy. During photosynthesis, plants use the sun´s energy to make glucose out of carbon dioxide and water, releasing oxygen. Photosynthesis means "putting together with light."

respiration : The process by which most living things convert the chemical energy in glucose into more accessible chemical energy in ATP. During respiration, cells break down glucose into carbon dioxide and water, using oxygen in the process. The overall process of cellular respiration is the reverse of photosynthesis.

stomata (STOH-muh-tuh) : Microscopic openings in the leaves of plants through which the plant takes in and releases gases. Stomata are found on the undersides of leaves.

TEACH

Activity 1: Energy Flows (Online)

Instructions

Have your student read through the Explore on her own. Reinforce and explain difficult concepts as needed.

Explore Suggestions:

Screen 5: Re-read the sentence: "Getting ATP from breaking up glucose is like taking a big check to the bank and coming home with dollar bills." Ask your student what cell organelle can do this, as the cell's "power plant." (Mitochondria)

Connect what your student learned in the Chemistry unit to the chemical reactions that take place in photosynthesis and respiration.

- The overall chemical reactions are:

  Photosynthesis:

  Light energy + $6CO_2$ + $6H_2O$ --> $C_6H_{12}O_6$ + $6O_2$

  Respiration:

  $C_6H_{12}O_6$ + $6O_2$ --> $6CO_2$ + $6H_2O$ + Energy in ATP

After this activity, check to see if your student can:

- Describe the process of cellular respiration.
- Describe the process of photosynthesis in plants.

If your student has difficulty with any of these concepts, you may wish to review the Explore with her and have her explain the key points on each screen.

Activity 2: Photosynthesis and Respiration Review (Offline)

Instructions

Teaching:

By comparing the processes of photosynthesis and cellular respiration, your student will become familiar enough with both to teach them to someone else. Have your student refer to the Explore for help with the review. Have your student complete the poster at the end of the activity and re-teach the content to you or someone else.

What to Expect:

Your student should be able to identify products and reactants in both photosynthesis and cellular respiration. Your student should also be able to describe both processes and understand that photosynthesis takes place in plant cells, while cellular respiration occurs in both plant and animal cells.

Answers:

See Answer Key.

Activity 3: Gas Exchange in Plants (Offline)

Instructions

Teaching:

Review the exchange of carbon dioxide and oxygen in plants. Carbon dioxide, which is given off by humans in respiration, is taken in by plants and used in photosynthesis. Oxygen, a product of photosynthesis, is given off by plants. Humans then breathe oxygen. These gases are exchanged through tiny openings in plants leaves called *stomata*. Your student will investigate the location of stomata by attempting to block them off, then observing the resulting condition of the plant.

Your student will start this activity before she reaches this lesson. As you see the plant leaves change, discuss what might be happening.

What to Expect:

The leaves that have petroleum jelly on their undersides will die. The other leaves will remain unchanged. Your student should understand that stomata are on the undersides of the leaves. When you block the stomata, the leaves cannot exchange gases and complete photosynthesis.

Answers:

Introduction

Oxygen and *carbon dioxide* are the gases involved in photosynthesis.

During photosynthesis, plants give off *oxygen* and take in *carbon dioxide*.

Hypothesis

Accept any reasonable hypothesis.

Analysis

1. The leaves that were coated on the top. They stayed green and healthy.
2. The leaves that were coated on the bottom. They turned yellow and died.
3. Their staying open is important to photosynthesis because they are involved in gas exchange. If they are blocked, carbon dioxide cannot be taken in and oxygen cannot be given off.

Conclusion

Stomata let gases that are used and given off in photosynthesis in and out.

ASSESS

Lesson Assessment: Photosynthesis and Respiration (*Online*)

Students will complete an offline assessment based on the lesson objectives. Print the assessment and have students complete it on their own. Use the answer key to score the assessment, and then enter the results online. The attached answer key is the most current and may not coincide with previously printed guides.

TEACH

Activity 4: Exhale! (*Offline*)

Instructions

Teaching:

Plants produce oxygen through photosynthesis, which requires sunlight. At night, when there is no sun, plants use oxygen and food as animals do, producing carbon dioxide. This is called *cellular respiration*. Your student will use an indicator to test for the evidence of carbon dioxide being given off by plants.

Troubleshooting:

You can purchase elodea at a pet store or other store that sells fish supplies.

What to Expect:

The indicator with the plant and the one exhaled into turn from blue to reddish. This indicates the presence of carbon dioxide. The indicator which is alone remains unchanged. Your student does not need to understand the chemical reaction behind this process but should understand the meaning of the color change in the indicator--that carbon dioxide is present.

Answers:

Observations

1. the jar with the Elodea that was kept in the dark
2. carbon dioxide

Conclusion

1. cellular respiration
2. photosynthesis
3. Photosynthesis uses carbon dioxide, so carbon dioxide in the water would have been used for photosynthesis.

Safety

When using the drinking straw in the Beyond the Lesson activity, exhale only. Do not inhale or drink the indicator.

Name _____   Date _____

Yes, Teacher! Answer Key

Imagine you are responsible for teaching someone about photosynthesis and cellular respiration. Follow the directions to help prepare these notes and diagrams for your student. Afterward, make a colorful poster to help you teach your lesson.

Taking Notes

Start with the basics. Provide your students with a few notes about photosynthesis and respiration. Write the chemical equations for both processes below. Use the Word Bank to help you.

Word Bank

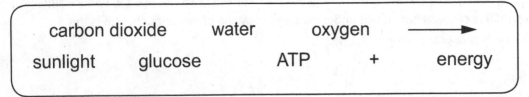

carbon dioxide   water   oxygen   ⟶

sunlight   glucose   ATP   +   energy

Photosynthesis:
                                    energy in
carbon dioxide + water + sunlight ⟶ glucose + oxygen

Respiration:
glucose + oxygen ⟶ carbon dioxide + water + energy in ATP

Yes, Teacher! Answer Key

Comparing

Once your students are familiar with photosynthesis and respiration, they should compare them. Comparing is a good way to see how things are either alike or different. Fill out the table to prepare for teaching your students how to compare photosynthesis and respiration.

	Where?	When?	Reactants?	Products?	Energy source?	Energy result?
Photo-synthesis	In cells that have chlorophyll	**when there is sunlight**	Carbon dioxide, water	**Glucose, oxygen**	**energy in Sunlight**	Energy is stored in glucose
Respiration	**In all cells**	All the time	**Glucose, oxygen**	Carbon dioxide, water	energy in glucose	**Energy is released in ATP**

Yes, Teacher! Answer Key

Drawing a Diagram

Every student learns in a different way. Some may need to see a "picture" or diagram of a process before they understand it completely. Help prepare a diagram for your students.

The diagram below compares photosynthesis and respiration. Fill in the blanks in the diagram to complete the comparison.

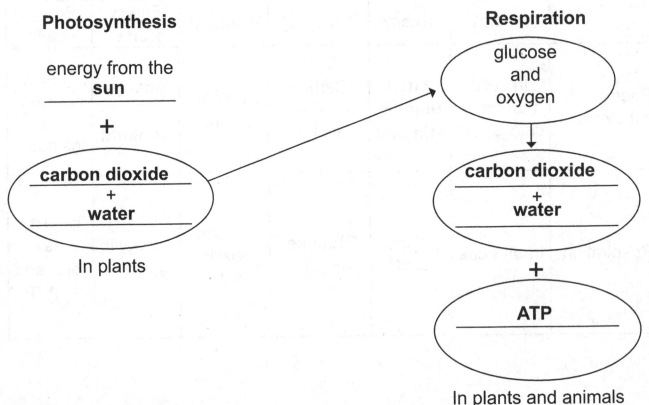

Teach Your Lesson

Use the answer key to check your answers in the Taking Notes, Comparing, and Drawing a Diagram sections. Next, make a poster to teach what you know about photosynthesis and respiration. Your poster should:

- Tell which processes happen in plants and which happen in animals
- List the products and reactants in both
- Explain where the energy comes from or goes to for both
- Use colors and pictures to explain what you are teaching

Share your poster with an adult. Use your poster to teach what you've learned about photosynthesis and respiration. Answer any questions the adult has after your lesson.

Name _____   Date _____

Lesson Assessment Answer Key

Word Bank

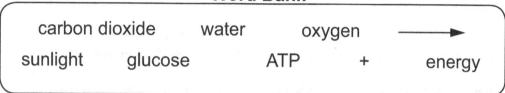

| carbon dioxide | water | oxygen | ⟶ |
| sunlight | glucose | ATP | + | energy |

1. Describe the process of photosynthesis. You may write an equation, draw a picture, or write an explanation. List all of the products and reactants. Explain whether this process takes place in animals, plants, or both. Use the word bank to help you.
   The student may either write or draw the following:
   carbon dioxide + water + sunlight ⟶ glucose + oxygen
   Photosynthesis occurs only in plants.

2. Describe the process of respiration. You may write an equation, draw a picture, or write an explanation. List all of the products and reactants. Explain whether this process takes place in animals, plants, or both. Use the word bank to help you.
   The student may either write or draw the following:
   glucose + oxygen ⟶ carbon dioxide + water + energy in ATP
   Respiration occurs in both plants and animals.

Learning Coach Guide
Lesson 5. Optional: The Cell Cycle

Cell division takes place constantly. The cell cycle involves different phases, known as *interphase*, *mitosis*, and *cytokinesis*. Explore these phases, view a dividing plant cell, and have your student make a model to help clarify the processes involved.

Lesson Objectives

- Identify and describe the four stages of mitosis: prophase, metaphase, anaphase, and telophase.
- Recognize that dividing plant and animal cells have a cycle with three phases: interphase, mitosis, and cytokinesis.
- Recognize that *interphase* is a period of growth and the copying of the genetic material.
- Recognize that *mitosis* is a period of division of the cell nucleus.
- Recognize that *cytokinesis* is a final event of cell division after mitosis.
- Demonstrate mastery of the skills taught in this lesson.

PREPARE

Approximate lesson time is 60 minutes.

Advance Preparation

- Wrap two forks, two spoons, and two knives in aluminum foil. They should still resemble forks, spoons, and knives.

Materials

For the Student

   📖 Time to Divide

     bags, paper grocery

     rubber band - several

     aluminum foil

     fork - plastic or metal (4)

     knife - plastic or metal-dull (4)

     spoon - plastic or metal (4)

     string

     yarn - different colors (2)

For the Adult

   📖 Time to Divide - Answer Key

Lesson Notes

As your student might be reminded, part of the cell theory is the understanding that cells come only from other cells. This observation is associated with an impressive phenomenon. Cells are able to reproduce, making fully functional copies of themselves. To understand in a real way how organisms reproduce, the student must at some point understand how cells reproduce.

In this lesson your student will be introduced to one of the most basic pieces of this puzzle--what happens with the chromosomes. Chromosomes contain the genetic material and all the instructions a cell needs to operate. Those instructions must be successfully passed along to a new cell as it is being made. This information is stored in the form of genetic material known as *DNA* .

- Chromosomes contain the genetic material carrying the instructions a cell needs to operate.

The process by which cells reproduce is called the *cell cycle.* It is the repeated set of things that cells do. Newly formed cells may themselves divide, as may the cells they form, and so on.

Before a cell can divide it usually needs to grow and always needs to make a copy of its chromosomes. The phase in which it does these things is called *interphase.* Interphase comes between the times when the cells are dividing. *Inter* means *between.*

When the cell is fully grown and a second copy of the genetic material is complete, the contents of its nucleus divide. This process is called *mitosis*. Mitosis itself has four phases: *prophase, metaphase, anaphase*, and *telophase.*

After telophase, *cytokinesis* is the final separation of the original cell into two cells.

During mitosis, the chromosomes begin to coil into thicker structures. Each chromosome has two identical copies of the genetic material, joined at one point. The membrane of the nucleus begins to break up as well. This frees the chromosomes to be separated into the two cells that will result. This first phase of mitosisis is called *prophase. Pro* means *before,* which is appropriate because this phase comes before all the others.

At the end of prophase, special molecules attach to the chromosomes and guide them to the middle of the cell. There, they line up as if they are on a plate or tray. This phase is called *metaphase.*

Next the special molecules pull each chromosome apart. The two identical copies of the genetic material separate and move toward the two ends of the cell. This is called *anaphase.*

Your student should notice what is happening here. Originally there is one chromosome with two connected copies of the genetic material. The chromosome then splits into two pieces, two new chromosomes from the original one, each new one with *one* copy of the genetic information. These two new identical chromosomes then separate, each on its way to go into one of the two new cells that will result.

The next step is *telophase* . The chromosomes have reached the two sides of the cell. At this point the chromosomes begin to uncoil and stretch out. A new nuclear membrane forms around each new set, creating the two new nuclei. Mitosis is complete, and one nucleus has become two.

The rest of the cell still needs to complete its division, which is the process called *cytokinesis.*

Finally, your student should understand that the newly made cells can now begin interphase, preparing to divide and make copies of themselves as well. This repetition is the essence of the cycle for dividing cells. Some cells exit the cycle, stopping divisions, and perform other functions for the rest of their lives.

Keywords and Pronunciation

chromosomes (KROH-muh-sohms) : Thread-like structures made of protein and DNA that contain the instructions for building, maintaining, and operating the cell. When a cell is ready for mitosis, its chromosomes begin to condense into thicker structures.

cytokinesis (siy-toh-kuh-NEE-suhs) : The process by which cells complete their division into new cells. Cytokinesis follows the end of mitosis in the cell cycle.

deoxyribonucleic (dee-AHK-sih-riy-boh-nyoo-clay-ick)

DNA : Deoxyribonucleic acid, the molecule carrying the genetic information found in every cell and unique to each individual. All the information an organism needs to live and reproduce is contained in its DNA.

mitosis (miy-TOH-suhs) : The process by which cell nuclei divide, separating the genetic material into two complete sets for the new cells. Mitosis follows a period of growth called interphase.

telophase (TEH-luh-fayz)

TEACH
Activity 1. Optional: A Cell's Busy Life (Online)
Instructions
Have your student read through the Explore on her own. Reinforce and explain difficult concepts as needed.
Explore Suggestions:
Screen 3: The video of a plant cell dividing may take a few minutes to load.

Screen 6: The idea that a chromosome has two copies of the genetic material splitting to form two separate but identical chromosomes, each with one copy, is important to understanding how genetic information is handled in cell division. Emphasize this part of the content and repeat the activity in the lesson several times to make this clear.

After this activity, check to see if your student can:

- Identify and describe the four stages of mitosis: prophase, metaphase, anaphase, and telophase.
- Recognize that dividing plant and animal cells have a cycle with three phases: interphase, mitosis, and cytokinesis.
- Recognize that *interphase* is a period of growth and the copying (duplication) of the genetic material.
- Recognize that *mitosis* is a period of division of the cell nucleus, with four stages of its own.
- Recognize that *cytokinesis* is a final event of cell division after mitosis.

If your student has difficulty with any of these concepts, you may wish to review the Explore with her and have her explain the key points on each screen.

Activity 2. Optional: Time to Divide: More About the Cell Cycle (Offline)
Instructions
Teaching:
This activity is a simple, active way to review and remember the phases involved in the cell cycle and the stages involved in mitosis. Enough information is provided for your student to do the activity on her own, but be available for assistance if needed and supervise her use of the knife. Have her repeat the process of cell division and explain it to you to show she understands.

Troubleshooting: You can use different-colored plastic utensils or different types of utensils instead of using metal utensils or wrapping the utensils in foil.

What to Expect:

Your student should be able to describe how cells reproduce and how chromosomes are copied and distributed to each new cell. She should understand what cells look like at each stage of cell division.

Safety

Use dull butter knives or plastic knives, and supervise your student while she is using the knives.

Activity 3. Optional: How Does a Cut Heal? *(Online)*

Instructions

Print the Activity Instructions if you have not already done so.

Safety

You may wish to preview any websites listed in this lesson.

Name _____   Date _____

Time to Divide Answer Key

Mitosis is the event in a cell's life when its nucleus divides. Place a check below next to the things you already know about mitosis. If there is something you do not know, go back and read the Explore again.

- Cells are always dying and new cells are always being formed.
- Cells contain genetic information in chromosomes.
- Every time a cell is preparing to divide, each chromosome makes an identical copy of itself.
- A new cell has the same exact genetic information as its "parent" cell.

Some things to think about:
- Do all cells of one organism look like one another?
- Do all cells of one organism have the same genetic information?
- How long does it take for one parent cell to become two "daughter" cells?

Study mitosis with a model cell. Imagine this is a body cell from an organism whose chromosomes look like forks, knives, and spoons. Follow the directions to model mitosis.

Make the Cell
1. Use one large piece of paper for your cell. Choose one color of yarn to be the cell membrane and another to be the nuclear membrane, which surrounds the nucleus.

2. Add six chromosomes to the cell: a wrapped fork, spoon, and knife and a plain fork, spoon and knife. Arrange the cell, membranes, and chromosomes on the floor as shown.

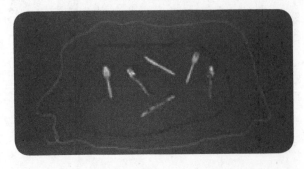

Time to Divide Answer Key

Interphase

During interphase, chromosomes are stretched out long and stringy and are copied. Imagine the chromosomes in your cell model are stretched out long and stringy.

1. Copy each chromosome by finding six more utensils exactly like the ones already in the nucleus.
2. With a rubber band, attach a wrapped fork to the wrapped fork, a plain fork to the plain fork, and so on. Imagine they are lengthened. Each pair of forks, spoons, and knives connected by a rubber band is one chromosome with two identical copies of its genetic material.

Prophase

During prophase, the copied chromosomes become shorter and the nuclear membrane disappears. Imagine the chromosomes in your model shorten.

- The amount of DNA in a chromosome that copied its genetic material is ____**double**____ the amount of DNA in a chromosome that did not copy its genetic material. (half, double, three times)
- The copies of genetic information in each chromosome are ____**the same**____. (the same, different, empty)

3. Remove the nuclear membrane from around the chromosomes.

Metaphase

During metaphase, the nuclear membrane is gone. Chromosomes line up along the middle of the cell.

4. Add "stringy molecules" stretched across the center of the cell.
5. Arrange the chromosomes in the center of the cell on the stringy molecules. The order does not matter and it is okay if the chromosomes are right-side up or upside down.

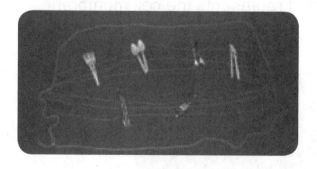

Time to Divide Answer Key

Anaphase

During anaphase, the stringy molecules pull each chromosome apart. The copies of genetic material separate and move toward the ends of the cell.

6. Separate your original chromosomes to form daughter chromosomes.
7. Move the chromosomes to the outer edge of the cell. Real chromosomes are flexible and bend in the middle as they are dragged through the cytoplasm. Imagine that your chromosomes bend as they are pulled apart.

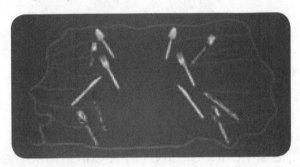

- Are the two sets of daughter chromosomes identical or different?
  identical
- Are the two sets of daughter chromosomes the same as those that were in the parent cell before they copied their genetic material? **yes**

Telophase

During telophase, the chromosomes stretch out again and two new nuclei are formed. Imagine your cell's chromosomes begin to stretch out again to become long and stringy.

8. Remove the stringy molecules from the chromosomes.
9. Cut the nuclear membrane string to create two new small nuclear membranes in the cell.
10. Start to pinch in the yarn that represents the cell membrane.

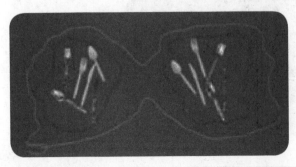

Time to Divide Answer Key

Cytokinesis

During this phase, one cell finishes becoming two. In animal cells, the cell membrane finishes pinching off. In plant cells, a new cell wall and membrane finish forming.

11. Divide your cell in half. Replace the long string representing the cell membrane with two shorter pieces of the same color representing new membranes of two new cells.

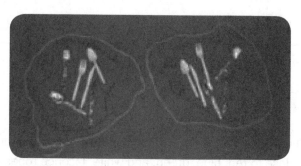

What Next?

The chromosomes in the two new cells will eventually start to copy themselves.

- What phase is this? **interphase**

- Does the parent cell still exist? **Not as a single cell. It has divided into two new cells.**

- How are the new cells related to each other? **They came from the same parent cell. They are copies of it and, therefore, the same as one another.**

- What was accomplished by mitosis? **Answers will vary but should include: A new cell was formed, the number of cells was increased, or the cell reproduced itself.**

Practice

You should realize that you can repeat this process over and over, just as cells continue to divide over and over again. Repeat the process, this time explaining it to someone else. Become familiar with the stages so that you can describe them when asked.

Learning Coach Guide
Lesson 6. Optional: DNA

DNA is made of molecular pieces twisted into a double helix and connected by bases, resembling a ladder. In this simple structure are the instructions for life--what proteins to make, what traits to pass on, and so on. Your student will study the structure of DNA, make a model, then observe real DNA from a living thing (peas).

Lesson Objectives

- Describe the structure of DNA as two twisted chains of molecular pieces with pairs of bases attached between them like rungs on a ladder.
- Explain that all the information an organism needs to live and reproduce is contained in its DNA.

PREPARE

Approximate lesson time is 60 minutes.

Advance Preparation

- To make a model of DNA, you will need black and red licorice sticks and either gumdrops, jelly beans, or marshmallows in colors close to red, blue, green, and white. Licorice ropes will work as well. If you use licorice ropes, you will not need to sew the licorice together.
- In addition to the common household items needed to extract DNA, you will need split peas and an enzyme such as meat tenderizer. If you do not have meat tenderizer, try pineapple juice or contact lens cleaning solution.

Materials

For the Student

    📖 Treat Yourself to DNA

        food - gumdrops or jelly beans

        household item - crayons

        household item - needle

        licorice - sticks, black

        licorice - sticks, red

        string - or fishing line

        toothpicks

        alcohol, rubbing

        blender

        household item - enzyme-see teacher guide

        household item - liquid detergent

        household item - plastic container

        peas - split- 100mL

        salt - 1 mL

        strainer

        test tube

        graduated cylinder

        measuring cup

        toothpicks - or other thin wood stick

        water

        household item - rubbing alcohol

        household item - small glass (6-8 oz)

        salt

        soap - liquid

For the Adult

    📖 Treat Yourself to DNA Answer Key

Lesson Notes

Just as a game with lots of different and conflicting rules is no game at all, any living thing, in order to stay alive and reproduce, needs a regular set of rules. Cells have just such a set of rules. They are like instructions carried within each cell that spell out everything the cell is to do, from surviving to creating more cells like itself. These cellular instructions can be thought of as letters that go together in different ways to spell out commands. What they literally are is the molecule known as *DNA*.

- Inside every cell is a set of instructions known as DNA.

DNA carries all the information in a cell's chromosomes. Scientists are currently making great headway in reading this information and understanding the instructions.

The DNA "alphabet" is only four letters long: G, C, A, and T. These letters stand for four different bases:

- Guanine
- Cytosine
- Adenine
- Thymine

These bases arrange themselves into the twisted ladder-shaped molecule that is DNA. How they do this is a bit complicated, but your student should be able to understand the essentials.

The bases line up along a long molecular chain. The chain is made from two other molecular pieces which link together. Sticking out from one side of the chain are the bases. The student is asked to picture them as four clothespins clipped to the chain, each a different color: Green, Crimson, Aqua and Tan (merely to keep G, C, A and T in mind).

Each clothespin connects at its free end with a clothespin of a certain color, and *only* that color. Every Green hooks up with a Crimson, and vice versa. Every Aqua hooks up with a Tan, and vice versa. This demonstrates how the bases actually pair up.

In this way, two chains of bases connect to each other to form a ladder. The ladder is twisty, like a spiral staircase. This twisty ladder, called a *double helix*, is the DNA molecule.

This process is far easier to understand with the help of some visual images. The graphics in the lesson illustrate the DNA molecule, where the bases are, and where they attach.

- The primary thing for which DNA gives instructions, and one of the most important, is building proteins. Proteins have many uses, from acting as building blocks for cells to acting as control levers in charge of cell functions. At the moment, however, your student need only understand that they are important to cells.

- Proteins are constructed out of smaller pieces known as *amino acids*.

There are twenty different kinds of amino acids. The ones the cell puts together, and the orders in which it arranges them, decide what kind of protein is made.

The amino acid called for is named in the DNA. For example, T-A-G essentially means "Add Isoleucine next." C-A-T means "Add Valine next."

It might seem to your student that an alphabet with only four letters could never spell out twenty separate names, but this is not so. In fact, there are 64 possible three-letter words that can be constructed out of the four DNA letters. That's more than enough to name 20 different amino acids. That means some amino acids can have more than one word in the DNA that corresponds to them. For example, both T-A-T and T-A-G mean "Isoleucine."

Keywords and Pronunciation

adenine (A-dn-een)

chromosomes (KROH-muh-sohms) : Thread-like structures made of protein and DNA which contain the instructions for building, maintaining, and operating the cell. Chromosomes contain the information that determines the eye, hair, skin color, and more in an individual.

cytosine (SIY-tuh-seen)

deoxyribonucleic (dee-AHK-sih-riy-boh-nyoo-clay-ick)

DNA : Deoxyribonucleic acid. This is the molecule, unique to each individual, carrying the genetic information to be found in every cell. All the information an organism needs to live and reproduce is contained in its DNA.

guanine (GWAH-neen)

thymine (THIY-meen)

TEACH
Activity 1. Optional: DNA--Instruction Manual for Life *(Online)*
Instructions
Have your student read through the Explore on his own. Reinforce and explain difficult concepts as needed.

Explore Suggestions:

Check your student's understanding by asking the following questions.

1. Where is DNA located? (on the chromosomes)
2. What is the "alphabet" of DNA? (the bases, or adenine, cytosine, guanine, and thymine--A, C, G, T)
3. Which bases are always linked together? (Adenine-A always pairs with thymine-T, and guanine-G always pairs with cytosine-C.)
4. The shape of DNA is a twisted ladder. What is the name for this shape? (double helix)
5. What important thing do DNA instructions tell a cell how to build? (proteins)

After this activity, check to see if your student can:

- Describe the structure of DNA as two twisted chains of molecular pieces, with pairs of bases attached between them like rungs on a ladder.
- Explain that all the information an organism needs to live and reproduce is contained in its DNA.

If your student has difficulty with any of these concepts, you may wish to review the Explore with him and have him explain the key points on each screen.

Activity 2. Optional: Treat Yourself to DNA *(Offline)*
Instructions
Teaching:

Review the importance of DNA. All genetic information is contained in this long molecule, a main component of the chromosomes. With just four pairs of bases, a cell is able build "you." This includes visible traits such as eye-color or left-handedness as well as traits that may not be so visible, such as the ability to understand complex math or to sing. Emphasize the amazing quality of this fact--that the billions of people on Earth are different from each other simply due to the arrangement of the bases in this tiny molecule.

What to Expect:

Your student will color, then make a candy molecule of DNA. She should be able to identify and describe the structure of DNA accurately following this activity.

Safety
This lesson involves eating or working with food. Before beginning, check with your doctor, if necessary, to find out whether your student will have any allergic reaction to the food.

The needle (used in Activity 2) is sharp. Supervise your student if necessary.

Activity 3. Optional: Look at Real DNA *(Online)*

Instructions

Teaching:

Reinforce the idea that DNA is present in all living things, which makes it possible to take out, or *extract*, DNA from anything alive. By clicking on the link to *How to Extract DNA from Anything Living*, you and your student will view the process for extracting DNA from split peas. Although this site is rich in information and photos, it is encouraged that you try to extract DNA yourself. This is a wonderful activity for students.

What to Expect:

If done correctly, your student should see long, white, stringy clumps of thousands of molecules of DNA.

Safety

Wear safety goggles during Activity 3.

Activity 3 should be done with close supervision from an adult.

Activity 4. Optional: D-N-A from Y-O-U *(Offline)*

Instructions

Print the Student Guide if you have not already done so.

Name _____   Date _____

Treat Yourself to DNA Answer Key

Scientists recognize that a long, thin, twisted molecule called *DNA* contains all the instructions for cells. Chromosomes are made up of DNA, like your body is made up of cells. These instructions include information about traits. If you've got brown eyes or are left-handed, you've got the instructions in your DNA to thank for that. Everyone all over the world is different from everyone else based on what is said in their DNA.

Learning about DNA takes a lot of hard work. A big break came in 1952 when a scientist named Rosalind Franklin produced pictures of DNA.

What does DNA look like? As you can see in the illustration, DNA has two strands that form a "double helix," a spiraling shape like a twisted ladder. DNA also has four bases: adenine, thymine, cytosine, and guanine.

When scientists model DNA, they generally use the same colors. Color the DNA illustration using the key.

Long chain links: red
Short chain links: black
Adenine: blue or aqua
Cytosine: red or crimson
Guanine: green
Thymine: tan

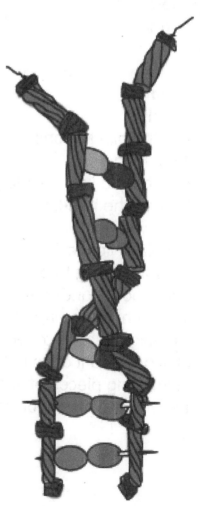

Make sure that every green is paired with a red and every blue is paired with a tan. The order does not matter.

Treat Yourself to DNA Answer Key

Notice that adenine and thymine are always paired together, as are guanine and cytosine. Notice, too, that the double helix in DNA is twisted.

Make a model
Use the illustration as a guide to make a DNA model.

Materials
licorice sticks, black
licorice sticks, red
fishing line or string, 2 pieces, 35 cm long
gumdrops, jelly beans, or marshmallows in colors close to red,
blue, green and tan (or white)
toothpicks
scissors
ruler (metric)
needle

Procedure
The Helix
1. Cut the black licorice into 18 small pieces, each about 1 cm long.
2. Cut the red licorice into 16 longer pieces, each 2 cm long.
3. Thread the needle with string or fishing line.
4. Start with the black licorice. Sew the string through the side of the black licorice.
5. Sew the string through the ends of the red licorice, so the red and black licorices are perpendicular.
6. On each line, string nine pieces of black licorice alternating with eight pieces of red. Wrap the string around the final piece of licorice so it does not fall off. You should have a total of 17 alternating pieces of licorice.
7. Lay the two lines side by side.

Treat Yourself to DNA Answer Key

The Bases

1. Study the code for the bases:
   Adenine: blue or aqua candy
   Cytosine: red or crimson candy
   Guanine: green candy
   Thymine: tan or white candy
2. Make pairs of bases, connecting the candy with a toothpick. Slide the candy all the way to the middle of the toothpick.

The Molecule

3. Connect the bases to the red licorice pieces to make a ladder.
4. You do not have to attach the bases in any order, but make sure they are attached to the red licorice and that green always pairs with red and blue with tan.
5. Once you've attached your bases, gently lift the model in the air using two hands.
6. Twist your model slightly to see the double-helix structure of DNA.

Questions

1. How do the bases pair up in a DNA molecule? How does your model help you understand this? **Adenine is paired with thymine and guanine is paired with cytosine. In the model colors represent the different bases and they are paired by color.**

2. What makes one DNA molecule different from another? How could you change your DNA model to show changes among DNA molecules? **One DNA molecule is different from another because its bases may be arranged in a different order. The same bases will always be paired, though. The model could be changed by rearranging the order of the candy bases.**

3. Can DNA make an exact copy of itself? **Yes**

4. How are chromosomes and DNA related? _____
   Chromosomes are made up of DNA.

Learning Coach Guide
Lesson 7. Optional: Heredity

An *inherited trait* is one that is passed from parent to offspring. This is possible due to information carried in the *DNA*, the main material that makes up chromosomes. Explore the role of genes and how they result in the passing of dominant and recessive traits. Learn to analyze how the forms of genes in parents affect the traits of their offspring. Survey other people for observable inherited traits.

Lesson Objectives

- Explain that traits are passed from parents to offspring and are determined by genes, with an individual having two copies of each gene, one from each parent.
- Distinguish between dominant and recessive forms of genes.
- Use a Punnett square to determine the genetic combinations and traits possible in offspring of a simple genetic cross.

PREPARE

Approximate lesson time is 60 minutes.

Materials

For the Student

    📖 Dominant and Recessive Traits

    household item - paper cup

    marker

    coins (3)

    tape - masking

    📖 Inheritance

For the Adult

    📖 Dominant and Recessive Traits Answer Key

    📖 Inheritance Answer Key

Lesson Notes

Many similarities among related people, from skin, eye, and hair color to height and build, are based on genetics. Everyone is unique. But we also inherit traits through chromosomes made up mainly of DNA.

- *Genetics* is the study of variations in characteristics in populations, and how similar characteristics pass from parents to their children (offspring).
- *Traits* are characteristics that vary from individual to individual.
- *Inherited traits* are ones that are passed down from parents to their offspring.

In this lesson the terms *parents* and *children* are used loosely for convenience, even for plants.

The beginning of our modern understanding of traits and inheritance came in the 1860s, in Czechoslovakia.

An Augustinian monk, Gregor Mendel, noticed patterns in pea plants he grew. Based on his observations, he hypothesized that "hereditary factors" are passed from plant to plant.

By maintaining strict control over which plants pollinated which others, Mendel studied how "parent" plants influenced "child" plants. In a famous experiment, he used plants with wrinkled peas and plants with smooth peas. Purebred plants result from breeding plants having a particular trait with each other for many generations, until they consistently pass the trait on to their offspring.

- Two purebred smooth-pea plants bred together produce only smooth-pea offspring.
- Two purebred wrinkly-pea plants bred together produce only wrinkly-pea offspring.

Mendel bred such plants. So far the pattern was simple.

Next, Mendel bred a smooth-pea parent with a wrinkly-pea parent. The result was always smooth-pea offspring.

A key insight of Mendel's comes from that observation. He hypothesized *dominant* and *recessive* factors transmitted to offspring. A dominant factor always "wins out" over a recessive one. In Mendel's experiment, the factor that makes peas smooth is dominant.

Next, Mendel bred together two of the offspring of his first experiment, in which he had crossed a smooth-pea plant and a wrinkly-pea plant. He found about 3/4 of the offspring this time were smooth-pea plants and about 1/4 were wrinkly-pea plants. This result seems confusing at first, but can be predicted by Mendel's hypothesis. The hypothesis can be expressed using a capital S to stand for the dominant factor, which produces smooth peas, and a lower-case s to stand for the recessive factor, which produces wrinkled peas (when no dominant smooth factor is present).

- Since the original parent plants were purebred, they each had two of the same factor. Call them SS and ss.
- All first-generation descendants received one factor from each parent. Each plant therefore ended up as an Ss.
- All second-generation descendants also received one factor from each parent.
- This results in four equally likely combinations: SS, Ss, sS, and ss.

Knowing that the presence of even one S means the plant will be smooth-pea, we can see why roughly a quarter of the second-generation plants would be wrinkle-pea and the rest smooth. Charts in the lesson may help in visualizing this.

We now know that the "factors" Mendel hypothesized correspond directly to what we now call *genes* . The genes are parts of DNA molecules, which make up chromosomes. Animals and plants have two of each type of chromosome, one from each parent. Therefore, individuals each have two copies of each gene for a trait. Some forms of a gene are dominant over others, though why exactly this is so is still being researched.

The point for your student here is that modern science is filling in details of how heredity works. However, Mendel discovered the basic structure well over a century ago, using nothing but careful observations, experiments, and creative thinking.

Keywords and Pronunciation

chromosomes (KROH-muh-sohms) : Thread-like structures, made of protein and DNA, that contain the instructions for building, maintaining, and operating the cell. Inherited traits are determined by the structure of the DNA that makes up the chromosomes.

genes : The parts of a chromosome that determine one or more characteristics, or groups of characteristics, that living things inherit from their parents. Genes determine your hair color, eye color, and more.

genetics (juh-NEH-tihks) : The study of how characteristics are passed on from parents to their offspring. Based on genetics, my daughter might have brown eyes like mine.

meiosis (miy-OH-suhs)

traits : Characteristics that vary from one individual to another. Inherited traits are passed on from parents to their offspring.

TEACH
Activity 1. Optional: Mendel and Genetics *(Online)*
Instructions
Have your student read through the Explore on her own. Reinforce and explain difficult concepts as needed.

Explore Suggestions:

Check your student's understanding by asking the following questions:

1. What is an inherited trait? (a trait passed from parent to offspring)
2. Do only humans have traits? (No, other animals and plants also have traits.)
3. What determines inherited traits? Where are they located? (genes, part of the DNA that makes up chromosomes)
4. What is a dominant form of a gene? (a form of the gene that will express its trait, even if forms of the gene that would express alternative traits are present)
5. What is a recessive form of a gene? (a form of the gene that will express its trait only if both copies of the gene are of that form, not if another, dominant, form of the gene is present)
6. Gregor Mendel thought there were two "factors" in a plant that were passed to it from its parents. What current scientific concept is used for these "factors"? (genes)

After this activity, check to see if your student can do the following:

- Explain that traits are passed from parents to offspring and are determined by genes, with an individual having two copies, one from each parent.
- Distinguish between dominant and recessive forms of genes.
- Use a Punnett square to determine the genetic combinations and traits possible in offspring of a simple genetic cross.

If your student has difficulty with any of these concepts, you may wish to review the Explore with her and have her explain the key points on each screen.

Activity 2. Optional: Traits and Using a Punnett Square *(Offline)*
Instructions
Teaching:

Each offspring receives genes from its parents that provide instructions about its traits. These traits are called *inherited traits.* The appearance of an offspring depends on what genes it receives from its parents. Eye color is an example of a trait that is passed from parent to offspring. Brown eyes are a dominant trait, while blue eyes are recessive. If you have blue eyes, then both of your parents must carry a blue-eyed gene. A *Punnett Square* is a tool that can be used to show possible ways genes can combine in offspring.

What to Expect:

Your student will toss coins to represent generations of offspring, then record the amount of each type of gene in each generation. Your student will then complete a Punnett Square. Your student should understand that the possible combinations found in the square are closely related to the numbers of each type of offspring in her tests. For example, if the Punnett Square shows that all offspring in Test 1 will have brown eyes, your student's observations should show that all offspring had brown eyes.

Your student should understand the difference between dominant and recessive traits and how to use a Punnett Square.

Activity 3. Optional: Inheritance *(Online)*

Instructions

Teaching:

A *dominant trait* is one that will always show up in offspring if its form of the gene is present. A *recessive trait* will only show up if both copies of a gene are the form for that trait. If one of the two copies of a gene is the form for the dominant trait, the dominant trait will be expressed.

Troubleshooting:

Have your student avoid surveying more than two members of the same family. Members of a family will have a tendency to exhibit the same traits based on the genes passed from parents to offspring.

What to Expect:

Your student will find that some traits are more common than others. This does not necessarily mean they are dominant traits--just that they appear more often.

Answers:

The dependent variable is the number of times the traits appear in the people surveyed.

Name _____   Date _____

Dominant and Recessive Traits Answer Key

You can use coins to find out about how genes and traits are inherited by offspring. *Traits* are characteristics that vary from one individual to the next. Genes, parts of the DNA molecule, determine what traits are passed on from one generation to the next.

Materials
masking tape
coins, 3
marker
paper cup

Procedure:
1. Place small pieces of masking tape on both sides of the coins.
2. Write a capital B on both sides of one coin. The B represents brown eyes. This coin represents a person with two genes for brown eyes.
3. On the other two coins, write a capital B on one side and a lowercase b on the other. These coins represent an individual with one gene for brown eyes (B) and one gene for blue eyes (b). These individuals are called "hybrid" because they have a mix of two forms of the eye color gene.

Which trait is dominant in this activity: brown eyes or blue?__brown eyes__

4. Now you will "combine" the genes. Place the chip representing a parent with two genes for brown eyes (BB) and one chip that represents a hybrid parent (Bb) into the cup.
5. Cover the cup and shake it. Spill the coins onto a table.
6. The letters that are facing up represent the genes one offspring of the two parents will have.
7. Observe which letters are facing up. Make a tally mark in the box on the chart labeled "Test 1" to record the genes the offspring has.
8. Repeat steps 4 – 7 a total of 20 times.
9. Add up the number of checks in each box. Record the total for each box.
10. Repeat steps 4 – 8 using two hybrid (Bb) coins. Record your offspring in the chart labeled "Test 2."

Dominant and Recessive Traits Answer Key

Observations

Test 1: BB x Bb

Parents	Offspring		
	BB (brown)	Bb (brown)	bb (blue)
BB x Bb			
Total after 20 tries			

Test 2: Bb X Bb

Parents	Offspring		
	BB (brown)	Bb (brown)	bb (blue)
Bb x Bb			
Total after 20 tries			

Using a Punnett Square

A *Punnett Square* is a tool that can be used to show possible ways genes from parents can combine in their offspring. It tells about *probability*, the chance something will happen. The letters stand for genes from each parent and are placed in the square first. Study the Punnett Square below.

Hybrid parent

	B	b
B		
B		

Pure parent

B = brown-eyed gene
b = blue-eyed gene

Dominant and Recessive Traits Answer Key

The next step is to combine the genes to show the possible ways they could be passed on to the offspring. Study the square to see this step. Circle the pairs of eye color genes that result in brown eyes. Put a triangle around the pairs that will result in blue eyes (none).

By looking at the square, you can see that each time the parents have offspring, there is a 100% chance that the offspring will have brown eyes.

Hybrid parent

Pure parent	B	b
B	(BB)	(Bb)
B	(BB)	(Bb)

B = brown-eyed gene
b = blue-eyed gene

Fill in the Punnett Square to the right to show the possible combinations of genes from two hybrid parents. Again, circle brown-eye pairs and put triangles around blue-eyed pairs.

Hybrid parent

Hybrid parent	B	b
B	(BB)	(Bb)
b	(bB)	△bb

B = brown-eyed gene
b = blue-eyed gene

When these parents have offspring, what is the probability that the offspring will have brown eyes? ____75%____
When these parents have offspring, what is the probability that the offspring will have blue eyes? ____25%____

Analysis
Look back at your observations from your tests.
1. In 20 test pairings, how many test offspring from a pure brown-eyed parent (BB) and a hybrid brown-eyed parent (Bb) had brown eyes? ____20____ How many had blue? ____0____

2. In 20 test pairings, how many test offspring from two hybrid brown-eyed parents (Bb and Bb) had brown eyes? __Answers will vary, but will likely be close to 15.__ How many had blue? __Answers will vary, but will likely be close to 5.__

Dominant and Recessive Traits Answer Key

3. Look back at your Punnett Squares. In Test 1, did you find that 100% of the offspring had brown eyes? _____Yes_____

4. The Punnett Square for Test 2 says there is a 75% chance the offspring will have brown eyes and a 25% chance the offspring will have blue eyes. If you performed Test 2 a total of 100 times, would you expect exactly 75 offspring to have brown eyes and exactly 25 offspring to have blue? Why or why not? **No. A Punnett Square displays the probabilities for each pairing of the parents. But in real life it should be close to 75 and 25.**

_____

_____

_____

5. How would your results be different if you tossed a hybrid coin (Bb) and a recessive coin (bb)? Make and complete a Punnett Square to answer the question. **There is a 50% chance that the offspring will have brown eyes and a 50% chance that the offspring will have blue eyes. About half of the offspring should be brown eyed and half blue eyed.**

_____

Hybrid parent

	b	b
B	Bb	Bb
b	bb	bb

(left axis label: Hybrid parent)

B = brown-eyed gene
b = blue-eyed gene

6. If you have time, try it.

Name _____   Date _____

Inheritance Answer Key

Eye color is just one of many interesting inherited traits. Survey a group of people to find out which traits are more common than others.

Hypothesis

Study the photos of inherited traits. You will survey 10 people about their traits. Which of the traits do you think will be the most common? Write a hypothesis._____

_____

Materials

paper
pencil
Example of Inherited Traits sheet

Procedure:

1. Study the examples of inherited traits.
2. Survey 10 people. Try to survey people other than family members.
3. Observe which form of each trait each person has.
4. Record your data in the chart. Make a tally mark for each person by the appropriate trait he or she has.

Observations

Trait	Tally
Dimples	
No dimples	
Hitchhiker's Thumb	
Regular thumb	
Can curl tongue	
Cannot curl tongue	
Short second toe	
Long second toe	
Left thumb on top when folding hands	
Right thumb on top when folding hands	
Unattached earlobe	
Attached earlobe	
Can make a "V" with fingers	
Cannot make a "V" with fingers	

Inheritance Answer Key

Analysis
Use the data from your observations to make a bar graph of a few traits.

	dimples	no dimples	can curl tongue	cannot curl tongue	unattached earlobe	attached earlobe

Conclusion
1. Which traits were most common?_____
   Answers will vary. Check your student's observations.

2. Because a trait is most common, does that mean it is dominant? For example, the gene for six fingers is dominant. You probably do not know many six-fingered people. Study the table below to help you answer the question. **No, just because a trait is common does not mean it is dominant. However, if a dominant trait is present in a parent, it will likely show up in at least some of the offspring.**

Inheritance Answer Key

Study the list of traits below.

	Dominant	**Recessive**
Earlobes	Unattached (F) (free)	Attached (f)
Dimples	Dimples (D)	No dimples (d)
Thumb	Hitchhiker's Thumb (H)	Regular thumb (h)
Tongue-rolling	Roller (R)	Nonroller (r)

3. Choose one of the traits for which to make a Punnett Square. You may cross pure parents or hybrid parents. Explain the results of your Punnett Square. **There is a 75% chance the offspring will have dimples and a 25% chance the offspring will not have dimples.**

Example

	D	d
D	**DD**	**Dd**
d	**Dd**	**dd**

Learning Coach Guide
Lesson 8: Unit Review and Assessment

Review cell and cell processes concepts covered during the unit. Your student will participate in a game called *Cell-ebrity Pranksters* to review. Then she will take the unit assessment.

Lesson Objectives

- Demonstrate knowledge and skills gained in this unit.
- Describe the three major ideas of the cell theory.
- Distinguish between plant and animal cells.
- Identify the major structures of cells and describe their functions (nucleus, cytoplasm, cell wall, cell membrane, chromosomes, mitochondria, and chloroplasts).
- Explain that different types of substances move across the cell membrane by means of diffusion, osmosis, and active transport.
- Explain that plant cells store energy through photosynthesis and that plant and animal cells release stored energy during respiration.
- Identify the major structures of the cell (such as cell membrane, cytoplasm, and nucleus) and describe their functions.
- Recognize various ways in which molecules are transported across the cell membrane.
- Describe the process of *photosynthesis* in plants.
- Recognize the major cell organelles (for example, endoplasmic reticulum, ribosomes, Golgi bodies, chloroplasts, chromosomes, mitochondria, and vacuoles) and describe their functions.
- Define *diffusion* as the process by which molecules move from areas of higher concentration to areas of lower concentration.
- Recognize that water moves through membranes by *osmosis*--diffusion of water through a semipermeable membrane.
- Explain that all the information an organism needs to live and reproduce is contained in its DNA.
- Demonstrate mastery of the skill taught in this unit.

PREPARE

Approximate lesson time is 60 minutes.

Materials

For the Student

    🖥 Question Review Table

TEACH
Activity 1: Cell-ebrity Pranksters (Online)
Instructions
Have your student read through the Explore on her own. Since this is a review, encourage her to return to any earlier lessons that might help her. Reinforce and explain difficult concepts as needed. If she has difficulty with any of these concepts, you may wish to review the Explore with her and have her explain the key points on each screen.

ASSESS
Unit Assessment: Cells and Cell Processes (Online)
Students will complete an offline Unit Assessment. Print the assessment and have students complete it on their own. Use the answer key to score the assessment, and then enter the results online. The attached answer key is the most current and may not coincide with previously printed guides.

TEACH
Activity 2. Optional: Unit Assessment Review Table (Online)

Activity 3. Optional: ZlugQuest Measurement (Online)

Name _____ Date _____

Unit Assessment Answer Key

Select the answer that best completes the question. (1 point each)

1. Movement of molecules from an area of higher concentration to one of lower concentration is called _____.
   A. osmosis
   B. mitosis
   Ⓒ diffusion
   D. active transport

2. Movement of molecules from an area of lower concentration to one of higher concentration with carrier molecules, using energy, is called _____.
   A. osmosis
   B. mitosis
   C. diffusion
   Ⓓ active transport

3. Diffusion of water across a membrane is called _____.
   Ⓐ osmosis
   B. mitosis
   C. cytokinesis
   D. active transport

4. DNA is found in the _____.
   A. vacuole
   Ⓑ chromosomes
   C. cell membrane
   D. Golgi body

Unit Assessment Answer Key

Word Bank

cells	traits	living	photosynthesis
respiration	DNA	cell	non-living

Use words from the word bank to complete the sentences. (2 points each)

5. All living things are made of _____**cells**_____.

6. Inside the chromosomes are molecules that contain all information an
   organism needs to grow and reproduce. This is its _____**DNA**_____.

7. The _____**cell**_____ is the basic unit of structure and function in living things.

8. Plant cells change the sun's energy to chemical energy
   during _____**photosynthesis**_____.

9. Living cells come only from other _____**living**_____ cells.

10. Cells change chemical energy into something usable during _____**respiration**_____.

11. Study the cell diagram and the chart. Label the organelles based on their
    descriptions. Fill in any missing descriptions in the chart. (1 point each)
    A-nucleus
    B-chloroplast
    C-mitochondria
    D-vacuole
    E-cell membrane
    F-cell wall

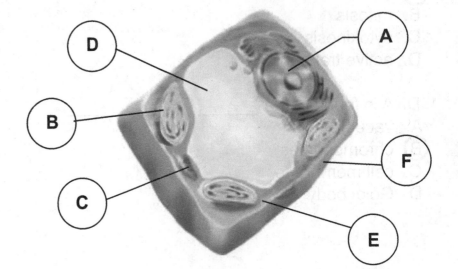

Unit Assessment Answer Key

12. Fill in the description or the name of the organelle. (2 points each)

	Cell Organelle	Description
A	Nucleus	**command center, directs cell activities**
B	**chloroplast**	in plants, changes sunlight energy into chemical energy through photosynthesis
C	**mitochondria**	changes chemical energy into energy that is useable by the cell
D	**vacuole**	fluid filled bubbles that store and digest food, get rid of waste, and pump water.
E	**chromosomes**	contains the genetic information for the cell and DNA
F	cell membrane	**acts as a skin for the cell and controls what goes in and out**
G	**cell wall**	rigid, gives plant cells their shape and support

Unit Assessment Answer Key

13. Read the following notes a student took about cells. Cross out any incorrect items and re-write them in the correct spot. Do not add any items. (1 point for each correctly changed item)

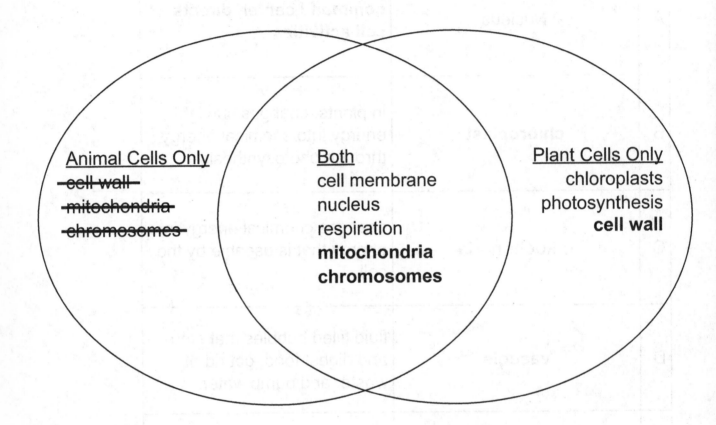

Animal Cells Only
~~cell wall~~
~~mitochondria~~
~~chromosomes~~

Both
cell membrane
nucleus
respiration
mitochondria
chromosomes

Plant Cells Only
chloroplasts
photosynthesis
cell wall

Learning Coach Guide
Lesson 1: Naming and Classifying Life

More than two million different species of organisms exist on Earth. Scientists name and group all of these organisms in order to study them. Organisms live everywhere- in the world's oceans, under decaying logs deep in the rain forest, and even high atop the mountains of the world.

All organisms and objects have names that make them unique. By using these names, we can communicate about these things more precisely. Learn more about one system that scientists use to classify organisms by their characteristics.

Lesson Objectives

- State that Carolus Linnaeus developed a system for naming and classifying organisms that is still used today.
- Recognize that an organism's scientific name is made up of the genus and species the organism belongs to.

PREPARE

Approximate lesson time is 60 minutes.

Advance Preparation

- If you have not yet received the book *The Kingdoms of Life: Classification*, skip to the next unit. Return to this one when the book arrives.

Materials

    For the Student
        Come Learn with Me: The Kingdoms of Life: Classification by Bridget Anderson
    📖 Scientific Classification Crossword Puzzle
    For the Adult
    📖 Scientific Classification Crossword Answer Key

Keywords and Pronunciation

Aristotle (AIR-uh-stah-tl)
Carolus Linnaeus (kah-raw-LOUS lih-NEE-uhs)
genus (JEE-nuhs)
species (SPEE-sheez)

TEACH
Activity 1: Let's Read (Online)

Instructions

Have your student read pages 6 through 11 of *The Kingdoms of Life: Classification*. He will learn about the ways in which scientists classify the many forms of life on Earth.

Activity 2: Scientific Classification Crossword *(Offline)*

Instructions

Print the Scientific Classification Crossword Puzzle if you have not already done so. Encourage your student to refer to the book as often as necessary to complete the puzzle.

ASSESS

Lesson Assessment: Naming and Classifying Life (*Online*)

Students will complete an online assessment based on the lesson objectives. The assessment will be scored by the computer. The attached answer key is the most current and may not coincide with previously printed guides.

Name ______________________________ Date ______________________________

Scientific Classification Crossword Puzzle Key

1 C			2 F	E	L	I	S			
L		3 L						4 G		
5 A	R	I	S	T	O	6 T	L	E		
S		N				W		N		7 L
S		N				O		U		I
I		A		8 T				S		B
F		E		R			9 U			R
I		U		E			S			A
C		10 S	P	E	C	I	E	S		R
A				S						Y
T					11 G	R	E	E	K	
I										12 D
13 O	F	F	S	P	R	I	N	G		O
N										G
	14 C	A	R	O	L	U	S			

Learning Coach Guide
Lesson 2: The Tools of Taxonomy

Carol Linnaeus created a system of classification to group organisms according to their shared characteristics. Learn about how modern systems of classification do the same thing.

Lesson Objectives

- Recognize that living things are classified by shared characteristics.
- Identify the seven major levels of classification: Kingdom, Phylum, Class, Order, Family, Genus, and Species.

PREPARE

Approximate lesson time is 60 minutes.

Materials

For the Student

Come Learn with Me: The Kingdoms of Life: Classification by Bridget Anderson

💻 Trees of the Pacific Northwest

For the Adult

💻 Trees of the Pacific Northwest Answer Key

Keywords and Pronunciation

Anton van Leeuwenhoek (AHN-tohn vahn LAY-ven-hook)

Carolus Linnaeus (kah-raw-LOUS lih-NEE-uhs)

conifer (KAH-nuh-fur)

dichotomous (diy-KAH-tuh-muhs)

genus (JEE-nuhs)

phylum (FIY-luhm)

species (SPEE-sheez)

TEACH
Activity 1: Let's Read (Online)

Instructions

Have your student read pages 12 to 15 to learn about the taxonomy of life on Earth.

Activity 2: Identifying Trees (Online)

Instructions

To identify the trees by name, your student will use a printout of six conifers of the Pacific Northwest and the website. The website provides an interactive dichotomous key for use in determining the type of tree. Mention that division is used for plants, not phylum, as stated in the book.

ASSESS
Lesson Assessment: The Tools of Taxonomy (*Online*)

Students will complete an online assessment based on the lesson objectives. The assessment will be scored by the computer. The attached answer key is the most current and may not coincide with previously printed guides.

TEACH
Activity 3. Optional: Dichotomous Keys (*Online*)
Instructions

Have your student develop his classification skills by identifying animals on a website.

Name _____   Date _____

Trees of the Pacific Northwest

Try your hand at identifying trees of the Pacific Northwest using a dichotomous key.

The needle-like leaves are not clustered on this tree. The needles are longer than 1/2 inch. The tiny pegs on the twigs are squared with sharp needles. ___**Spruce**___

This tree has leaves that are needle-like. The needles are clustered with 2-5 needles. ___**Pine**___

The needle-like leaves on this tree are not clustered and are longer than 1/2 inch. There are no pegs on the twigs. The buds are small and pointed, and they are not found clustered on the twig. As you turn the pointed needle over, it is white underneath. ___**Redwood**___

The flattened leaves on this tree are scale-like. All of the leaves are short and sharp. **Giant Sequoia**___

The needle-like leaves, which measure longer than 1/2 inch, are not clustered. There are no pegs on the twigs. The buds are not large but are pointed. The terminal buds are not clustered. As you turn the needle over, it is green underneath. ___**Yew**___

Learning Coach Guide
Lesson 3: Phylogenetic Trees and the Kingdoms of Life

All life on Earth can be classified into one of six kingdoms: Archaebacteria, Eubacteria, Protista, Fungi, Planta, and Animalia.

Lesson Objectives

- Name the six kingdoms: Archaebacteria, Eubacteria, Protista, Fungi, Planta, and Animalia.

PREPARE

Approximate lesson time is 60 minutes.

Materials

For the Student

Come Learn with Me: The Kingdoms of Life: Classification by Bridget Anderson

  📖 What Would Linnaeus Say?

For the Adult

  📖 What Would Linnaeus Say? Answer Key

Keywords and Pronunciation

Animalia (A-nuh-MAY-lee-uh)

archaebacteria (AHR-kee-bak-TIHR-ee-uh)

eubacteria (YOO-bak-TIHR-ee-uh)

fungi (FUN-jiy)

genetics (juh-NEH-tihks) : The study of how characteristics are passed on from parents to their offspring. Based on genetics, my daughter might have brown eyes like mine.

phylogenetic (fiy-loh-juh-NEH-tihk)

Protista (proh-TIS-tuh)

TEACH
Activity 1: Let's Read (Online)
Instructions

The science of *genetics* explains why some organisms are more similar than others. It helps explain why members of the same families have similar characteristics. Have your student read pages 16 through 19 to learn more.

Activity 2: What Would Linnaeus Say? *(Offline)*

Instructions

Print What Would Linnaeus Say? if you have not already done so. Encourage your student to refer to his book often as he completes the worksheet.

ASSESS

Lesson Assessment: Phylogenetic Trees and the Kingdoms of Life (*Online*)

Students will complete an online assessment based on the lesson objectives. The assessment will be scored by the computer. Complete Solutions are provided in the Assessment Answer Key.

Name _____   Date _____

What Would Linnaeus Say? Answer Key

A. For each organism listed below, circle the organism that is more closely related genetically. (Hint: use the diagram in your book for help.)

1. **human girl**   (human man)   female duck

2. **sunflower**   worm   (daisy)

3. **green algae**   (moss)   cnidarian

4. **snake**   (lizard)   flatworm

5. **crustacean**   (insect)   fungi

B. Use the Word Bank below to complete this paragraph.

> **Word Bank**
> genetics   fossils   phylogenetic tree   different   similar   identical

The branch of science that studies relationships between

organisms is __genetics__. Children in the same family have

nearly __identical__ genes, while birds and insects have very

__different__ genes. Once genetic relationships are understood,

scientists can show the relationships by drawing a __phylogenetic

tree__. By studying genes from __fossils__ and genes

from animals living today, scientists gain evidence about how

modern organisms are related to ancient organisms.

What Would Linnaeus Say? Answer Key

C. Matching: Draw lines to connect the name of each kingdom with its description.

Kingdom Archaebacteria

Kingdom Eubacteria

Kingdom Protista

Kingdom Fungi

Kingdom Planta

Kingdom Animalia

They live in wet places. Examples are algae and slime molds.

Their cells use chlorophyll to help them make their own food.

These single-cell organisms live in extreme environments, such as deep-sea vents.

Fish, insects, and mammals belong to this kingdom.

These common bacteria are found everywhere on Earth.

These eukaryotic organisms absorb nutrients from dead or living plants and animals.

Learning Coach Guide
Lesson 4: Kingdom Archaebacteria

Some organisms live in the most extreme environments on Earth--sometimes in places where no other living creatures could survive. Bacteria from Kingdom Archaebacteria can live in some of the coldest and hottest places on Earth. Your student will take closer look at these fascinating organisms.

Lesson Objectives

- Identify two characteristics common to organisms in Kingdom Archaebacteria (live without oxygen, live in extreme environments both hot and cold).
- Identify one organism in Kingdom Archaebacteria.

PREPARE

Approximate lesson time is 60 minutes.

Materials

For the Student

Come Learn with Me: The Kingdoms of Life: Classification by Bridget Anderson

🖥 Solving the Riddles of Bacteria

For the Adult

🖥 Solving the Riddles of Bacteria Answer Key

Keywords and Pronunciation

archaebacteria (AHR-kee-bak-TIHR-ee-uh)

cyanobacteria (siy-A-nuh-bak-TIHR-ee-uh)

eubacteria (YOO-bak-TIHR-ee-uh)

halophile (HA-luh-fiyl)

methanogen (muh-THAN-uh-juhn)

TEACH
Activity 1: Let's Read (Online)

Instructions

Have your student read pages 20 to 21 to learn about Archaebacteria.

Activity 2: Bacteria Riddles (Offline)

Instructions

Print Solving the Riddles of Bacteria if you have not already done so. Encourage your student to refer to the book often as he solves the riddles.

ASSESS

Lesson Assessment: Kingdom Archaebacteria (*Online*)

Students will complete an online assessment based on the lesson objectives. The assessment will be scored by the computer. Complete solutions are provided by the Assessment Answer Key.

Name _____ Date _____

Solving the Riddles of Bacteria Answer Key

Read each riddle, then solve it. (Hint: You'll find help in your text.)

1. I am shaped like a rod, and I live in the intestines of animals. What kind of bacteria am I? (Hint: my name starts with the letter S.)
   shigella _____

2. If you've ever had a "strep throat," then I was responsible. I am the bacteria that causes throat infections. Who am I?
   streptococcus _____

3. I love hot environments--even the hottest ones! I can also live without oxygen. What kind of bacteria am I?
   thermophile _____

4. All bacteria are made up of me. I am a type of cell. Who am I?
   prokaryotic _____

5. Because I can live in extremely salty environments, I can live in the Great Salt Lake in Utah. What kind of bacteria am I?
   halophile _____

6. If you want to see the structure and behavior of bacteria, you need to use me. (I'm not just an ordinary microscope!)
   electron microscope _____

7. I am a disease caused by the dangerous bacteria called *Borrelia burgdofferri*. **Lyme disease** _____.

SUPER CHALLENGE: Name this term! The first one has been done for you.

1. All rod-shaped bacteria are called **bacillus** _____.
2. All round bacteria are called **coccus** _____.
3. All spiral bacteria are called **spirillum** _____.
4. This term refers to things that love extreme environments. Archaeophiles are one example. **extremophile** _____.

Learning Coach Guide
Lesson 5: Kingdom Eubacteria

All bacteria not part of Kingdom Archaebacteria belong to Kingdom Eubacteria. This kingdom's microscopic world includes eubacteria that live near us, even within our own bodies.

Lesson Objectives
- Identify a characteristic common to organisms in Kingdom Eubacteria (live in less extreme environments).
- Identify one organism in Kingdom Eubacteria.

PREPARE

Approximate lesson time is 60 minutes.

Materials
> For the Student
>> Come Learn with Me: The Kingdoms of Life: Classification by Bridget Anderson
>> 🖳 Name That Eubacteria or Virus!
> For the Adult
>> 🖳 Name That Eubacteria or Virus! Answer Key

Keywords and Pronunciation
amoeba (uh-MEE-buh)
cyanobacteria (siy-A-nuh-bak-TIHR-ee-uh)
eubacteria (YOO-bak-TIHR-ee-uh)
paramecium (PAIR-uh-MEE-shee-uhm)
thermophile (THUR-muh-fiyl)

TEACH
Activity 1: Let's Read (Online)

Instructions
Have your student read pages 22 through 23 to learn about Kingdom Eubacteria. Explain that the root word *troph* means *nourishment*, and learn how these tiny organisms get their food.

Activity 2: Name That Eubacteria or Virus! (Offline)

Instructions

Print the Name That Eubacteria or Virus! worksheet if you have not already done so. Encourage your student to refer to his book often as he determines which kind of eubacteria matches each description. Emphasize to your student that viruses are not eubacteria, though they appear in this section. Scientists cannot agree on whether viruses are even alive.

ASSESS

Lesson Assessment: Kingdom Eubacteria (*Online*)

Students will complete an online assessment based on the lesson objectives. The assessment will be scored by the computer. The attached answer key is the most current and may not coincide with previously printed guides.

TEACH

Activity 3. Optional: Microbiologists Do! (*Online*)

Instructions

Once your student discovers the kinds of things that microbiologists do, he might decide that this is the career for him! Have him visit each part of this extensive website. He'll read about microbiologists, learn about microbes, solve Microbe Mysteries, and enjoy other online adventures.

Name _____ Date _____

Name That Eubacteria or Virus! Answer Key

Read each description, then write *photo-autotroph*, *chemo-autotroph*, *heterotroph*, or *virus* in the space next to each.

1. Decomposers are members of this group. **heterotroph**

2. Some of these are considered "nitrogen-fixing machines." **chemo-autotroph**

3. Not all scientists think these are even alive. **virus**

4. They make their food from sunlight. **photo-autotroph**

5. To reproduce, they must use the cell of another organism. **virus**

6. Sulfur, iron, and nitrogen are needed to make food for this group. **chemo-autotroph**

7. They contain chlorophyll. **photo-autotroph**

8. They absorb nutrients from other organisms because they can't make their own food. **heterotroph**

9. Their bodies are not made of cells, though they can use the cells of others. **virus**

10. Photosynthesis lets them make food. **photo-autotroph**

11. Parasites are part of this group. **heterotroph**

12. These are not actually bacteria. **virus**

13. Their name means "self-nourishment from chemicals." **chemo-autotroph**

14. Cyanobacteria are part of this group. **photo-autotroph**

Learning Coach Guide
Lesson 6: Kingdom Protista

Members of Kingdom Protista include many one-celled organisms that thrive in wet environments. Amoebas, paramecia, molds, and algae are all part of this group. Find out about some of the types of protists, and learn about these organisms that are all around you.

Lesson Objectives

- Identify two characteristics common to organisms in Kingdom Protista (thrive in wet environments, most are single celled).
- Identify two organisms in Kingdom Protista (protozoa, amoeba, paramecium, algae, seaweed, water mold, slime mold).
- State that protists are often grouped according to whether they are plant-like, fungus-like or animal-like.

PREPARE

Approximate lesson time is 60 minutes.

Advance Preparation

- You will need 10 jars and 20 cups of distilled water for the optional Soap and Algae activity.

Materials

For the Student

    Come Learn with Me: The Kingdoms of Life: Classification by Bridget Anderson

    🖥 Protists by Alphabet

Optional

    🖥 How Does Soap Affect Algae Growth?

    jar, storage (10)

    measuring cup

    soap - 1 1/2 cups of liquid soap

    spoon - measuring

    water - distilled, 20 cups

    water - lake, stream, tap, or bay, 20 cups

    water - tap

For the Adult

    🖥 Protists by Alphabet Answer Key

Keywords and Pronunciation

algae (AL-jee)

amoeba (uh-MEE-buh)

eukaryotic (yoo-KAHR-ee-AH-tihk)

fungi (FUN-jiy)

paramecium (PAIR-uh-MEE-shee-uhm)

Protista (proh-TIS-tuh)

protozoa (proh-tuh-ZOH-uh)

TEACH
Activity 1: Let's Read *(Online)*

Instructions

Have your student read pages 24 through 27 to learn about Kingdom Protista.

Activity 2: Protists by Alphabet *(Offline)*

Instructions

Print out the Protists by Alphabet worksheet if you have not already done so. Have your student use his book for help in finding the answers. Point out that some of the answers have been provided.

ASSESS

Lesson Assessment: Kingdom Protista (*Online*)

Students will complete an online assessment based on the lesson objectives. The assessment will be scored by the computer. Complete Solutions are provided in the Assessment Answer Key.

TEACH
Activity 3. Optional: Soap and Algae *(Offline)*

Instructions

Print the How Does Soap Affect Algae Growth? if you have not already done so. Help your student prepare each jar of water, then guide him in adding soap. Remind him to record his observations each day for five days, then have him explain his conclusion. He should discover that adding soap inhibits the growth of algae.

Name _____ Date _____

Protists by Alphabet Answer Key

Read the clues, then fill in the answer. The first letter of each answer is given for you. Some of the answers have been completed for you.

Amoebas look like jelly. To move, they have to change shape.

Bacteria and pieces of dead organisms are food for slime molds.

Ciliates are covered with little hairs. They move in a corkscrew fashion.

Downy **mildew** have killed a lot of crops. The rotten potato in your book is infected with it.

Eggyolk **slime** grows on a stick. There is a picture of one in your book.

Flagellates move by flapping flagella. Many are parasitic.

Goldfish can look furry when water molds grow on them. There is a picture of one in your book.

Hairy is one way to describe a paramecium. Its many cilia make it look this way.

Irish **Potato** **Famine** is a famous disaster that took place in the 1840s. A downy mildew caused it to happen.

Jelly-like blobs are one way the book describes amoebas.

Kelp is a large, complex type of algae that can grow into forests underwater.

Protists by Alphabet Answer Key

Lakes and oceans are home to the Kingdom Protista.

Molds described in your book are slime and water.

Nori is the Japanese name for a kind of seaweed called Porphyra nereocystis.

Oxygen is produced by algae. Humans need it to breathe.

Paramecium is a very complex protozoan.

Q is not the first letter of any protist in your book.

Red, brown, and green are some of the colors algae can have.

Sporozoa live in the cells of other living things. They are very tiny parasites.

Transparent is how the bodies of amoebas and most protists look, which means you can see through them.

Ulva is also called sea lettuce. It is a kind of alga.

Vorticella is a ciliate. It is not mentioned in your book.

Water **molds** look like cotton. Some grow on dead algae, and some grow on living organisms.

X is not the first letter of any of the words in this section.

Yamadaella **caenomyce** is a kind of algae that grows in the Red Sea, but it is not shown in your book.

Zoomastiginia is the group that flagellates belong to. (This information is not in the book.)

Learning Coach Guide
Lesson 7: Kingdom Fungi

Have you ever seen a piece of fruit with fuzz on it? Do you like mushrooms on your pizza? The fuzz and the mushrooms are both fungi! Look deeper into the diverse world of Kingdom Fungi.

Lesson Objectives

- Identify characteristics common to organisms in Kingdom Fungi (grow best in warm, moist conditions; reproduce through spores).
- Identify two organisms in Kingdom Fungi (mushroom, lichens, some molds, yeast).

PREPARE

Approximate lesson time is 60 minutes.

Advance Preparation

- If you choose to do the Rising Yeast optional activity, plan to set aside about an hour and twenty minutes for it.

Materials

For the Student

    Come Learn with Me: The Kingdoms of Life: Classification by Bridget Anderson

    🖳 Spreading Spores

    clay

    cotton ball (8)

    stick

    balloon - long and slender

    tape

Optional

    🖳 Rising Yeast

    food - cup of flour (2)

    food - pkg. of rapid-rise yeast

    food - tsp. honey (6)

    food - tsp. sugar (6)

    household item - clothespins (24)

    household item - drinking straws (24)

    household item - medium-sized bowls (4)

    stopwatch - watch or timer

    measuring cup

    ruler, metric

    spoon

    spoon - measuring

Keywords and Pronunciation
fungi (FUN-jiy)
fungus (FUNG-guhs)

TEACH
Activity 1: Let's Read (Online)
Instructions
Have your student read pages 28 through 29 to learn about Kingdom Fungi.

Activity 2: Spreading Spores (Offline)
Instructions
Your student will create a model of the spore-bearing structure of a bread mold. The balloon is the spore case and the cotton balls are the spores. Remind him to follow the directions carefully.

Answer Key:
If they were real spores, each would grow into a fungus. The fungi would grow wherever the spores fell.

ASSESS
Lesson Assessment: Kingdom Fungi (*Online*)
Students will complete an online assessment based on the lesson objectives. The assessment will be scored by the computer. The attached answer key is the most current and may not coincide with previously printed guides.

TEACH
Activity 3. Optional: Rising Yeast (Offline)
Instructions
Yeast is an important ingredient in many breads, and sugar helps yeast rise. Your student will cook up his own experiment to discover these facts. He should come to these conclusions and note them on the worksheet:

1. The dough would not have risen without yeast.
2. Sugar and honey made the yeast more effective. The honey had a greater effect on the yeast in the amounts used. The dough with honey rose higher.

Learning Coach Guide
Lesson 8: Kingdom Planta

Humans would not be able to survive without plants. We need plants for food and for oxygen. Get ready for a journey through Kingdom Planta.

Lesson Objectives

- Identify characteristics common to organisms in Kingdom Planta (all except mosses are vascular, all use photosynthesis to get nutrients).
- Identify two plants in Kingdom Planta.
- Describe *vascular plants* as plants that have systems for transporting water, sugar, and minerals, whereas *nonvascular plants* lack these structures.
- Explain how sugar, water, and minerals are transported in vascular plants.
- Compare characteristics of gymnosperms and angiosperms.

PREPARE

Approximate lesson time is 60 minutes.

Advance Preparation

- You will need two fresh stalks of celery for the Up Goes the Water activity.

Materials

For the Student

Come Learn with Me: The Kingdoms of Life: Classification by Bridget Anderson

📖 Compare Angiosperms and Gymnosperms

📖 Up Goes the Water

celery - stalk (2)

For the Adult

📖 Compare Angiosperms and Gymnosperms Key

Keywords and Pronunciation

angiosperm (AN-jee-uh-spuhrm)

gymnosperm (JIM-nuh-spuhrm)

Sequoia sempervirens (sih-KWOY-uh sem-puhr-VIY-ruhns)

TEACH
Activity 1: Let's Read *(Online)*

Instructions

Have your student read pages 30 through 37 to explore Kingdom Planta.

Activity 2: Compare Angiosperms and Gymnosperms *(Offline)*

Instructions

Looking carefully at the features of a tree can tell whether the tree is an *angiosperm* or a *gymnosperm*. Print the Compare Angiosperms and Gymnosperms worksheet if you have not already done so, and encourage your student to refer to his book as necessary.

Activity 3: Up Goes the Water *(Online)*

Instructions

Print Up Goes the Water if you have not already done so. Help him set up the materials so he can observe the water traveling up the celery stalk.

Safety

This activity involves working with food. Before letting your student handle the food, be certain he is not allergic to it.

ASSESS

Lesson Assessment: Kingdom Planta *(Online)*

Students will complete an offline assessment based on the lesson objectives. Print the assessment and have students complete it on their own. Use the answer key to score the assessment, and then enter the results online. The attached answer key is the most current and may not coincide with previously printed guides.

Name _____   Date _____

Compare Angiosperms and Gymnosperms Key

Do you remember the characteristics of angiosperms and gymnosperms? Look at each characteristic listed in the table, then write
YES if it applies and NO if it does not apply.

Characteristic	Angiosperms	Gymnosperms
Do they have seeds?	Yes	Yes
Do they have flowers?	Yes	No
Do most have needle or scale-like leaves?	No	Yes
Do most have woody cones?	No	Yes

Now that you have reviewed the characteristics, write a paragraph
that compares angiosperms with gymnosperms. How are they
alike? How are they different?

**Answers will vary but should include the characteristics
listed above, with specific examples.**

_____

_____

_____

_____

_____

_____

_____

Name: Date:

Lesson Assessment Answer Key

Kingdom Planta

Gymnosperms and angiosperms are both vascular plants within the Kingdom Planta. Which description is common to **both** gymnosperms and angiosperms?

The correct answer is B, seeds.

Organisms from the Kingdom Planta are found throughout the environment around us. Mosses are members of this kingdom. Which organisms belong to the Kingdom Planta? Select the **two** correct answers.

The correct answers are B, redwood trees, and D, daisies.

All of the organisms in the Kingdom Planta, except mosses, are vascular. Which description is common to all organisms in the Kingdom Planta?

The correct answer is D, use photosynthesis to get nutrients.

What is the difference between vascular and nonvascular plants?

The correct answer is B, have systems for transporting water and minerals.

How are water and minerals transported in vascular plants? Explain in a short paragraph that uses the terms *xylem*, *phloem*, and *shoots*.

Vascular plants have roots that absorb the water and minerals from the soil. Hollow tubes called xylem carry the water and minerals up through the plant to the shoots where the plant makes its food. Then the phloem moves the food made in the shoots to all the other parts of the plant.

Learning Coach Guide
Lesson 9: Kingdom Animalia

Worms, flamingoes, and bears are all part of Kingdom Animalia.

Lesson Objectives

- Identify characteristics common to organisms in Kingdom Animalia (multicellular, need to get food from an outside source).
- Identify two organisms in Kingdom Animalia that are vertebrates.
- Identify two organisms in Kingdom Animalia that are invertebrates.
- Recognize that Kingdom Animalia includes organisms that are vertebrates and invertebrates.

PREPARE

Approximate lesson time is 60 minutes.

Materials
For the Student
Come Learn with Me: The Kingdoms of Life: Classification by Bridget Anderson

Keywords and Pronunciation
Animalia (A-nuh-MAY-lee-uh)

TEACH
Activity 1: Let's Read (Online)
Instructions
Have your student learn about Kingdom Animalia by reading pages 38 through 45.

Activity 2: Learn More About Kingdom Animalia (Online)
Instructions
By visiting the National Aquarium Baltimore and Saint Louis Zoo websites, your student will see many examples of Kingdom Animalia. Encourage him to record the names of as many animals as possible on the table he will make in his Science Notebook.

ASSESS

Lesson Assessment: Kingdom Animalia (Online)
Students will complete an online assessment based on the lesson objectives. The assessment will be scored by the computer. Complete Solutions are provided in the Assessment Answer Key.

Learning Coach Guide
Lesson 10: Unit Review and Assessment

The seven levels of classification help us understand the many kinds of living things in the world. Your student will use these new concepts to design a zoological garden, and then test his knowledge of taxonomy.

Lesson Objectives

- Name the six kingdoms (Archaebacteria, Eubacteria, Protista, Fungi, Planta, and Animalia) and identify organisms from each.
- Demonstrate mastery of the skills taught in this unit.
- Explain how sugar, water, and minerals are transported in vascular plants.
- Recognize that living things are classified by shared characteristics, and that there are seven major levels of classification: kingdom, phylum, class, order, family, genus, and species.
- Compare the characteristics of the various groups of plants.

PREPARE

Approximate lesson time is 60 minutes.

Materials

For the Student

📖 Question Review Table

TEACH
Activity 1: The Carolus Linnaeus Zoological Garden (Online)
Instructions

Most zoos concentrate on animals, but there are five other kingdoms of living organisms. Your student will assist an architect in planning a zoological garden that includes all the kingdoms. Encourage your student to be as detailed as possible in his plans. He should include a very wide variety of living things from each kingdom, and he should decide how to present these organisms to the public.

ASSESS

Unit Assessment: Taxonomy of Plants and Animals (Online)

Students will complete an offline Unit Assessment. Print the assessment and have students complete it on their own. Use the answer key to score the assessment, and then enter the results online. The attached answer key is the most current and may not coincide with previously printed guides.

TEACH
Activity 2. Optional: Unit Assessment Review Table (Online)

Activity 3. Optional: ZlugQuest Measurement (Online)

Name: _____ Date: _____

Unit Assessment Answer Key

Taxonomy of Plants and Animals

Circle TRUE or FALSE.

TRUE or FALSE: Gymnosperms reproduce using seeds, but angiosperms do not.

The correct answer is False.

TRUE or FALSE: Living things are classified by shared characteristics.

The correct answer is True.

TRUE or FALSE: All gymnosperms lose their leaves in the winter.

The correct answer is False.

Linnaeus created seven levels of classification. Circle the names of the seven levels.

The correct answers are:

Kingdom   **Order**   **Phylum**   **Family**

Genus   **Species**   **Class**

The first two letters of each of the seven kingdoms have been provided. Complete the name of each kingdom, and then write the letter to match the kingdom with its description.

A. Planta

B. Animalia

C. Eubacteria

D. Archaebacteria

E. Protista

F. Fungi

E. Paramecium and algae

C. Heterotroph

F. Mushrooms and lichens

A. Angiosperms and gymnosperms

B. Fish, insects, and mammals

D. Single-cell organisms such as halophiles

How do vascular plants get the water and minerals that they need to live and grow? Be sure to include the words *xylem*, *phloem*, and *roots* in your answer.

Answers may vary but should include this: Vascular plants get water and minerals they need from soil. The roots absorb the water and minerals. Hollow tubes called xylem carry the water and minerals up through the plant to the shoots. The plant makes its own food in the shoots. The plant makes its own food in the shoots. Then the phloem moves the food made in the shoots to all the other parts of the plant.

Learning Coach Guide
Lesson 1: The Miracle of Life

Billions of animals live on Earth. Inside each of their bodies are special systems constantly adjusting to changes in the environment around and within their bodies.

Do you ever wonder how the bodies of animals work? How are animals able to regulate their body temperatures? How do their coats change colors? These questions, and many more, are part of the area of study called *animal physiology.*

If you are working on this unit out of order and have not yet received the book, please go on to another unit and return to this one later.

Lesson Objectives

- Recognize that all body systems play a role in maintaining a constant internal environment.
- Describe how bones and muscles interact to cause movement.

PREPARE

Approximate lesson time is 60 minutes.

Materials

    For the Student

        Come Learn with Me: How Bodies Work: Animal Physiology by Bridget Anderson

        🖥 Cooling Effect

    For the Adult

        🖥 Cooling Effect Answer Key

Keywords and Pronunciation

cell membrane : The fatty outer covering of a cell. The cell membrane allows certain substances to pass through it.

cytoplasm (SIY-tuh-pla-zuhm) : The jelly-like matter of a living cell that is outside the nucleus. Organelles are contained in cytoplasm.

homeostasis (HOH-mee-oh-STAY-suhs) : A state of balance reached through reactions within a cell or organism. Homeostatis is important for cells to function efficiently.

lysosomes (LIY-suh-sohm) : An organelle in animal cells that contains powerful enzymes. Lysosomes contain chemicals that process substances within the cell.

mitochondria (miy-tuh-KAHN-dree-uh) : The organelles that produce usable chemical energy. There can be many mitochondria in a single cell.

nutrient : Any substance that provides nourishment. Proteins are a type of nutrient for the body.

organelle (or-guh-NEL) : A tiny structure in the cytoplasm of the cell. Animal cells contain different types of organelles.

TEACH
Activity 1: Let's Read (Online)
Instructions
Have your student read pages 6 through 15 to learn about the discipline of animal physiology.

Activity 2: Cooling Effect (Offline)
Instructions
Print Cooling Effect if you have not already done so. Have your student describe what it is like to sweat. Explain to her that this is one way that the body cools itself in hot weather.

ASSESS
Lesson Assessment: The Miracle of Life (Online)
Students will complete an offline assessment based on the lesson objectives. Print the assessment and have students complete it on their own. Use the answer key to score the assessment, and then enter the results online. The attached answer key is the most current and may not coincide with previously printed guides.

Name _____   Date _____

Cooling Effect Answer Key

Do you know how your body cools down? This experiment will show you.

Materials
Thermometer   Clock
Cotton ball   Graduated cylinder
Rubbing alcohol 10mL

Procedure
1. Lay the thermometer on a table. Let it come to room temperature. Record the temperature on a piece of paper.
2. Moisten a cotton ball with rubbing alcohol.
3. Spread the cotton ball into thin strands. Spread a thin layer of the wet cotton across the bulb of the thermometer.
4. Blow across the wet cotton 15 times.
5. Record the temperature on the thermometer.

Conclusions
What happened to the temperature after adding the cotton ball with the rubbing alcohol?
Blowing on the cotton causes the thermometer to record a lower temperature.

How is this like the body's response when it gets too hot?
Answers will vary but should include these: During warm weather, the sweat glands release more fluids on the surface of the skin. The evaporation of sweat removes heat from from the skin, causing the skin to feel cooler.

_____

_____

Name _____ Date _____

Miracle of Life Lesson Assessment Answer Key

1. TRUE or FALSE: One body system maintains the constant internal environment of the whole body. **False**

2. Describe how muscles and bones work together to help the human body move. In your answer, be sure to include the words *muscles*, *bones*, *ligaments*, and *tendons*.

The human body moves by using muscles together with with bones. Ligaments hold the bones together while tendons attach the muscles to the bone. When the muscles shorten, the other muscle pair stretches, allowing a body part to move.

Learning Coach Guide
Lesson 2: The Nervous and Endocrine Systems

The *nervous system* is the command center of an animal's body. This system helps maintain the homeostasis of the body. The hormones from the endocrine system also help to maintain a balance.

Lesson Objectives

- Identify the parts of the human nervous system and their function (brain, spinal chord, and nerves).
- Identify some parts of the human endocrine system and their function (pituitary gland, thyroid gland, adrenal gland, and pancreas).

PREPARE

Approximate lesson time is 60 minutes.

Materials

For the Student

Come Learn with Me: How Bodies Work: Animal Physiology by Bridget Anderson

📖 The Endocrine System

For the Adult

📖 The Endocrine System Answer Key

Keywords and Pronunciation

adrenal (uh-DREE-nl)

endocrine (EN-duh-kruhn)

gland : An organ that produces special chemicals called hormones. The adrenal glands produce adrenaline when the brain instructs them to do so.

motor neurons : Nerve cells that deliver orders from the brain and spinal chord telling the body what to do. Motor neurons tell the body when it needs to move.

nerve : A thin fiber that sends messages between the brain or spinal chord and other parts of the body. The optic nerve passes messages between the brain and the eye.

nerve cord : A strand of nerve tissue that runs the length of the body and forms the main part of an animal's nervous system. The spinal cord is an example of a nerve cord.

nerve net : A simple nervous system containing nerve cells but no brain. Some invertebrates, such as jellyfish, have a nerve net.

pancreas (PAN-kree-uhs)

pituitary (puh-TOO-uh-tair-ee)

sensory neurons : Nerve cells that gather information from the body and carry it to the brain and spinal chord. Sensory neurons alert the brain when the body is damaged in some way.

TEACH
Activity 1: Let's Read (Online)
Instructions
Have your student read pages 16 through 21 to learn about the nervous system and the endocrine system.

Activity 2: The Endocrine System (Offline)
Instructions
Print out the Endocrine System if you have not already done so. Remind your student to refer to the book as often as necessary.

ASSESS

Lesson Assessment: The Nervous and Endocrine Systems (Online)
Students will complete an online assessment based on the lesson objectives. The assessment will be scored by the computer. The attached answer key is the most current and may not coincide with previously printed guides.

Name _____   Date _____

The Endocrine System Answer Key

Use the Word Bank to label the main structures of the endocrine system.

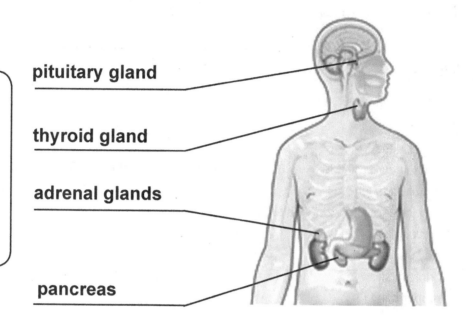

Word Bank

adrenal glands
thyroid
pituitary gland
pancreas

pituitary gland

thyroid gland

adrenal glands

pancreas

Describe the function of each gland here. Two have been completed for you.

1. Adrenal glands **produce adrenalin for the body**

   _____

2. Thyroid gland **produces hormones that influence the growth and development of the body**

3. Pituitary gland **controls the growth of the human body, among other things**

4. Pancreas **produces enzymes and hormones that help with digestion**

Learning Coach Guide
Lesson 3: The Respiratory System

Animals cannot survive without oxygen. But how does oxygen get into animal bodies? Learn more about the respiratory systems of animals and investigate for yourself!

Lesson Objectives

- Identify the parts of the human respiratory system (nose, mouth, trachea, lungs, diaphragm).
- Describe how the respiratory system exchanges carbon dioxide and oxygen in the lungs.
- Demonstrate mastery of the skills taught in this lesson.

PREPARE

Approximate lesson time is 60 minutes.

Materials

For the Student

Come Learn with Me: How Bodies Work: Animal Physiology by Bridget Anderson

📖 Lung Model

bag, clear plastic - zipper-closed

bottle, plastic - 2 Liter

clay - small ball

drinking straw

rubber band (3)

balloon

scissors, round-end safety

tape - masking

Keywords and Pronunciation

alveoli (al-VEE-uh-liy) : Tiny air sacs in each lung through which oxygen enters and carbon dioxide leaves the blood. Alveoli are shaped like bunches of grapes.

bronchi (BRONG-kiy) : The tubes in the lungs through which air passes. Human have two bronchi--one for each lung.

carbon dioxide : A gas with no color or smell that is a mixture of carbon and oxygen. Animals breathe out carbon dioxide.

diaphragm (DIY-uh-fram) : A dome-shaped muscle below the lungs that assists with breathing. When you breathe in, your diaphragm expands.

spiracle (SPIHR-uh-kuhl)

trachea (TRAY-kee-uh) : A tube in animals used for drawing air into the body. Air passes from the nose and mouth into the trachea.

TEACH

Activity 1: Let's Read *(Online)*

Instructions

Have your student read pages 22 through 25 to learn about the respiratory system.

Activity 2: Lung Model *(Offline)*

Instructions

Print out The Lung Model if you have not already done so. Remind your student which structures are part of the respiratory system. After she builds her model, ask her to explain it to you.

Your student should explain what happens with oxygen and carbon dioxide in the lungs in this way: Oxygen enters the mouth and nose and travels down the trachea. It then moves into one of two bronchi that then delivers it to each lung. The diaphragm helps the lungs expand and fill with oxygen as this is happening. The bronchi branch off into alveoli and the gases go directly into the bloodstream. The red blood cells drop off the oxygen in the blood and pick up the carbon dioxide that needs to leave the body. The carbon dioxide travels back out through the bronchi, trachea, and finally through the nose and mouth.

ASSESS

Lesson Assessment: The Respiratory System *(Offline)*

Students will complete an offline assessment based on the lesson objectives. Print the assessment and have students complete it on their own. Use the answer key to score the assessment, and then enter the results online. The attached answer key is the most current and may not coincide with previously printed guides.

Name: _____   Date: _____

Lesson Assessment Answer Key

The Respiratory System

Circle the correct answer for each of the following.

What is the name of the large dome-shaped muscle under your lungs that helps you breathe?

The correct answer is D. Diaphragm.

If your mouth is closed, which part of your respiratory system takes in air first as you breathe?

The correct answer is A. Nose.

What is the name of the long tube that runs from your mouth and connects to the lungs?

The correct answer is C. Trachea.

Which part of the respiratory system, which also helps with food digestion, helps the body take in air?

The correct answer is B. Mouth

Which part of the respiratory system is the spongy organ that takes in air through the trachea?

The correct answer is D. Lungs.

Describe how the respiratory system exchanges carbon dioxide and oxygen in the lungs. Use the words *carbon dioxide*, *lungs*, *trachea,* and *bronchi* in your answer.

Answers will vary but should include these: As oxygen enters the mouth and nose, it travels down the trachea. It then moves into one of two bronchi that then delivers it to each lung. The diaphragm helps the lungs expand and fill with oxygen as this is happening. The bronchi branch off into alveoli. The alveoli are surrounded by blood vessels and gas exchange occurs here. After the red blood cells leave the lungs they are rich in oxygen. They carry this oxygen to the body's cells. They drop off the oxygen where needed, and then pick up carbon dioxide that has left cells. The carbon dioxide travels back out through the bronchi, trachea, and finally, through the nose and mouth.

Learning Coach Guide
Lesson 4: The Circulatory System

The *circulatory system* is the transport system of the body. It is the key to how food materials move through the body.

Lesson Objectives
- Explain how blood flows through the human heart.
- Recognize that the circulatory system transports oxygen and nutrients to cells while carrying carbon dioxide and other wastes for removal.
- Recognize that some organisms have no circulatory system, some have an open circulatory system, and others have a closed circulatory system.
- Identify the structures of the heart (atria, ventricles, valves, major veins and arteries).
- Demonstrate mastery of the skills taught in this lesson.

PREPARE

Approximate lesson time is 60 minutes.

Materials
For the Student

Come Learn with Me: How Bodies Work: Animal Physiology by Bridget Anderson

🖳 A Circulation Model

For the Adult

🖳 A Circulation Model Answer Key

Keywords and Pronunciation
capillary : A small blood vessel that carries blood between the arteries and the veins. Capillaries are the smallest, thinnest blood vessels.

TEACH
Activity 1: Let's Read *(Online)*
Instructions
Have your student read pages 26 through 29 to learn about the circulatory system.

Activity 2: A Circulation Model *(Offline)*

Instructions

Print A Circulation Model if you have not already done so. Have your student use the model to explain to you how open circulatory systems work.

Activity 3: How Does Blood Flow Through a Human Heart? *(Online)*
Instructions

Encourage your student to spend a lot of time on the Medtropolis site. She should visit each section that relates to the human heart.

ASSESS

Lesson Assessment: The Circulatory System (*Online*)

Students will complete an offline assessment based on the lesson objectives. Print the assessment and have students complete it on their own. Use the answer key to score the assessment, and then enter the results online. The attached answer key is the most current and may not coincide with previously printed guides.

Name _____   Date _____

A Circulation Model Answer Key

Not all organisms have a closed circulatory system. Investigate another model of circulation--the open circulatory system.

Materials
1 T. honey
1 drop of food coloring, any color
1 paper plate

Procedure
1 Place a spoonful of honey on a paper plate.
2. Add a drop of food coloring around one edge of the honey.
3. Gently tilt the paper plate to make the honey flow in different directions.

Conclusions
What happened to the food coloring? **It spread throughout the honey.**

Compare this model to the open circulatory system. **This is a model for how the circulation system works in an organism that has an open circulatory system. There are no veins that transport the blood throughout the body, unlike in the human circulatory system.**

Would this circulatory system be efficient for a human? Why or why not? **This circulatory system would be inefficient for a human. The human body is too large to move all of the blood throughout the body with this system.**

Name: _____   Date: _____

Lesson Assessment Answer Key

The Circulatory System

Circle the correct answer for each.

TRUE or FALSE: All organisms have a closed circulatory system.

The correct answer is B. False.

Which structure of the heart acts like an automatic door that closes once blood enters a chamber and forces it to exit in the proper direction.

The correct answer is B. valves.

Which part of the heart takes blood from the veins and pumps it into a ventricle?

The correct answer is A. atria.

What is the name of one of the lower chambers of the heart that receives blood from the upper chambers and pumps it into the arteries?

The correct answer is D. ventricles.

What is the name of the blood vessels that carry blood from the heart to all the other parts of the body?

The correct answer is C. arteries.

The circulatory system transports oxygen and nutrients to cells of the body. What does it remove from the body?

The correct answer is B. carbon dioxide and other wastes.

Explain how blood flows through the human heart. Be sure to include the words *lung, valve, atrium*, and *blood* in your answer.

The heart has four chambers in which blood flows through. The upper chambers are called the atria, while the lower chambers are called the ventricles. At the opening of each chamber is a valve to make sure that once blood enters the chamber, it flows in the correct direction. Blood enters the heart through the right atrium. It flows into the right ventricle and is pumped into the lungs. Blood full of oxygen from the lungs enters the left atrium. It flows into the left ventricle and is pumped into the body's arteries to be carried to the body's cells.

Learning Coach Guide
Lesson 5: The Digestive System

The digestive system plays a key role in getting nutrients into the bloodstream and wastes out of the body.

Lesson Objectives
- Sequence the digestion process.
- Identify the structures involved in the digestive process and describe their function (mouth, esophagus, stomach, small intestine, large intestine, and liver).
- Demonstrate mastery of the skills taught in this lesson.

PREPARE

Approximate lesson time is 60 minutes.

Materials
For the Student

    Come Learn with Me: How Bodies Work: Animal Physiology by Bridget Anderson

Optional

    📖 Folds

    glass container, large - slender

    paper towels (5)

    tape - masking

Keywords and Pronunciation
enzymes (EN-ziym) : A protein in the body. Some enzymes help break food down into usable nutrients during digestion. Enzymes in your saliva break down starch, starting the process of digestion.

esophagus (ih-SAH-fuh-guhs)

peristalsis (pair-uh-STAWL-suhs) : Muscle contractions that move food, waste, and other contents through some digestive organs in the body. Peristalsis of the esophagus helps you swallow food.

vacuole (VA-kyuh-wohl) : A storage organelle of the cell. Some vacuoles help transport food molecules across a cell membrane.

TEACH
Activity 1: Let's Read (Online)
Instructions
Have your student read pages 30 through 33 to learn about the digestive system.

Activity 2: The Parts of the Digestive System *(Online)*
Instructions
The digestive system is complex but very logical. Your student will view a website with detailed pictures of each part of the system. Encourage her to copy the pictures carefully into her notebook; if she has any difficulty with this, have her print the screen first.

ASSESS
Lesson Assessment: The Digestive System (*Online*)
Students will complete an offline assessment based on the lesson objectives. Print the assessment and have students complete it on their own. Use the answer key to score the assessment, and then enter the results online. The attached answer key is the most current and may not coincide with previously printed guides.

TEACH
Activity 3. Optional: Folds *(Offline)*
Instructions
Your student will fold sheets of paper towels, then soak them in water. After she has completed the experiment, have her explain to you the ways in which paper towels are similar to human intestines.

Answers:
1. The four sheets of paper towel removed much more water than the one sheet.
2. The folded sheets of paper towels act just like the tissues inside the human intestines. The four sheets that you folded four times absorbed more water than the one sheet that you folded the same number of times. The four sheets had more available surface area to absorb the water from the jar. As the surface area of the paper towels increased, so did their ability to absorb more liquid. The human intestine provides a large surface area for absorption. Its walls are lined with fold after fold of absorbing tissue. The intestines of the human body are folded many times, making them able to absorb nutrients during the digestive process.

Name _____   Date _____

The Digestive System Answer Key

Circle the correct answer for each.

1. Which part of the human body begins to break down food first?
   A. small intestine
   B. liver
   (C.) mouth
   D. esophagus

2. Which long tube carries food from the mouth to the stomach?
   A. small intestine
   B. liver
   C. mouth
   (D.) esophagus

3. What is the name of the muscular, sac-shaped organ located below the liver where food is digested?
   A. small intestine
   (B.) stomach
   C. mouth
   D. esophagus

4. What is the name of the long, coiled part of the digestive system connected to the stomach that finishes digesting the last bits of food?
   (A) small intestine
   B. liver
   C. mouth
   D. esophagus

5. Which large organ in the human body located above the stomach helps digest food and clean the blood?
   (A.) trachea
   B. liver
   C. mouth
   D. large intestine

Name _____ Date _____

The Digestive System Lesson Assessment Key

6. What is the name of the thick, lower end of the digestive tract where solid waste is gathered and leaves the body?
   - A. trachea
   - B. liver
   - C. mouth
   - D. large intestine

7. Place the following steps of digestion in the correct order. Label the first step of digestion A, the second step B, and so forth.

   F_____ The remaining food passes into the large intestine. Water is absorbed from the large intestine and the rest of the material is stored as solid waste.

   B_____ Saliva rushes into the mouth and mixes with the broken-down food.

   C_____ The food travels down the esophagus.

   A_____ The teeth in the mouth bite off a piece of food. The teeth continue to break the food into smaller pieces.

   D_____ The muscles of the stomach churn the food and continue to break it down.

   E_____ The broken down food, called *chyme*, enters the small intestine.

Learning Coach Guide
Lesson 6: The Excretory System

Learn about the special filters and transport systems in the excretory system of the body.

Lesson Objectives

- Identify the organs of the excretory system and describe their function (lungs, liver, kidneys, and skin).
- Explain how the excretory system removes cellular waste from the blood, converts it to urine, and stores it in the bladder before it leaves the body.
- Demonstrate mastery of the skills taught in this lesson.

PREPARE

Approximate lesson time is 60 minutes.

Materials

For the Student

Come Learn with Me: How Bodies Work: Animal Physiology by Bridget Anderson

📖 Excretory System Crossword Puzzle

For the Adult

📖 Excretory System Crossword Puzzle Answer Key

Keywords and Pronunciation

bladder : The organ that stores liquid waste before it leaves the body. The bladder can stretch to hold about a pint of urine.

nephron (NEH-frahn) : A tiny fiber in the kidney in which the filtering of water and waste from the blood takes place. There are approximately one million nephrons in one of your kidneys.

ureter (YUHR-uh-tuhr)

ureter tube (YUHR-uh-tuhr) : A tube through which urea is transported from the kidneys to the bladder. A valve at the base of the ureter tube prevents urine from flowing back into the kidney.

TEACH
Activity 1: Let's Read (Online)
Instructions

Have your student read pages 34 through 37 to learn about the excretory system.

Activity 2: The Excretory System Crossword Puzzle (Offline)

Instructions

Print out the Excretory System Crossword Puzzle if you have not already done so. Have your student solve the puzzle. Remind her that she should refer to the book as often as necessary.

ASSESS

Lesson Assessment: The Excretory System (Online)

Students will complete an offline assessment based on the lesson objectives. Print the assessment and have students complete it on their own. Use the answer key to score the assessment, and then enter the results online. The attached answer key is the most current and may not coincide with previously printed guides.

Name _____   Date _____

Excretory System Crossword Puzzle Answer Key

¹B	L	A	D	D	E	R		²A	N	³U	S	
A							⁴K			R		⁵F
⁶C	A	R	B	O	N	D	I	O	X	I	D	E
T							D			N		C
E		⁷M					N			A		E
R		⁸U	R	E	A		E			R		S
I		S					Y			Y		
A		C		⁹W	A	S		¹⁰T	E			¹¹N
		L						W		¹²T		E
¹³U	R	E	T	H	R	A		O		W		P
R		S								O		H
E			¹⁴U									R
T			R									O
E			I		¹⁵M	A	N	U	R	E		N
R			N									
	¹⁶S	W	E	A	T		¹⁷P	E	L	V	I	C

Name: _____   Date: _____

Lesson Assessment Answer Key
The Excretory System

Circle the correct answer for each question. (1 point each)

1. Carbon dioxide is a waste product from breathing. Which organ of the body, which is attached to the trachea, pushes carbon dioxide out of the body?

    The correct answer is B. lungs.

2. Which organ, located just below the diaphragm, turns waste materials from the blood into urea?

    The correct answer is A. liver.

3. Which organ releases salt and liquid waste from the body through its pores and glands?

    The correct answer is D. skin.

4. Which pair of organs, located in the lower back, collects liquid and waste from the blood?

    The correct answer is C. kidneys.

5. How does the human urinary system filter waste from the blood, store it and then get rid of it? Please include the word *kidneys*, *urine*, and *bladder* in your answer. (3 points)

    The blood transports urea, old cells, excess salt, and unwanted water to the kidneys. Waste and water from the blood are filtered in the kidneys, producing urine. Urine flows through ureter tubes and is stored in the bladder. When the bladder gets full, urine exits the body through the urethra.

Learning Coach Guide
Lesson 7: The Immune System and the Reproductive System

The immune system "fights" to protect the body from disease and illness.

Lesson Objectives

- Describe some reproduction differences between animals.
- Identify the structures involved with the immune system and describe their function (bone marrow, white blood cells, and lymphocytes).
- Identify two ways we can work to keep our immune system healthy (get vaccines, eat healthful foods).
- Recognize that different organisms reproduce through division or fusion.

PREPARE

Approximate lesson time is 60 minutes.

Materials

For the Student

Come Learn with Me: How Bodies Work: Animal Physiology by Bridget Anderson

🖳 Immune and Reproductive System Riddles

For the Adult

🖳 Immune and Reproductive System Riddles Key

Keywords and Pronunciation

antibody : A protein that fights infection. Lymphocytes manufacture antibodies to protect the body against disease.

blood marrow : A soft, reddish substance that is inside bones and produces blood cells. Doctors sometimes examine blood marrow to check on the immune system's health.

lymphocyte (LIMP-fuh-siyt) : A kind of white blood cell that produces antibodies to fight infection. Lymphocytes recognize different types of infection, and then send the correct antibodies to fight the infection.

pathogen (PA-thuh-jen) : Something that can cause a disease. Bacteria is a pathogen.

vaccine (vak-SEEN) : A substance containing weakened, dead, or living organisms that causes a body's immune system to fight against disease. The vaccine against polio is so effective that disease has been eliminated in many countries.

white blood cell : A colorless blood cell that is part of the body's immune system. A white blood cell protects the body against infection.

TEACH
Activity 1: Let's Read *(Online)*
Instructions
Have your student read pages 38 through 45 to learn about the immune system and the reproductive system.

Activity 2: Immune and Reproductive System Riddles *(Online)*
Instructions
Print out Immune and Reproductive System Riddles if you have not already done so. Encourage your student to refer to the book as often as necessary to answer the riddles.

ASSESS
Lesson Assessment: The Immune System and the Reproductive System
(Online)
Students will complete an online assessment based on the lesson objectives. The assessment will be scored by the computer. The attached answer key is the most current and may not coincide with previously printed guides.

Name _____ Date _____

Immune and Reproductive System Riddles

Read each riddle, then solve it. (Hint: You'll find help in your text.)

1. Animal life continues because of me. I am the system by which animals create new life. What am I? __the reproductive system__

2. I am an animal that splits up into pieces, making copies of myself in order to reproduce. What am I? __Answers may vary, but should include: a flatworm__

3. Some animals, such as a sea anemone, reproduce by division. But I am a different form of reproduction in which two cells from two animals of the same species join together to form a new animal. What form of reproduction am I?__fusion__

4. Animals' bodies are designed to protect against things like me. I also called a "germ." What am I? __a pathogen__

5. When an animal gets sick, I start producing lots of white blood cells. What am I? __bone marrow__

6. I am made of many layers and am the first line of an animal's defense against germs. What am I? __skin__

7. I am a type of medicine that teaches an animal's body to produce antibodies ahead of time. What am I? __a vaccine__

8. I am made in an animal's bone marrow. I move around an animal's body through the bloodstream, and I am also the second line of defense against germs. What am I? __a white blood cell__

9. I am one type of white blood cell that can remember the pathogens I come in contact with. I help other white blood cells find germs by creating antibodies that attach to the germs. What am I? __a lymphocyte__

10. I am made of many tissues, organs, and systems including the reproductive and immune systems. These parts and systems work together to help me function. What am I? __the animal body__

Learning Coach Guide
Lesson 8: Unit Review and Assessment

Encourage your student to review the book before she takes the assessment.

Lesson Objectives

- Recognize that all body systems play a role in maintaining a constant internal environment.
- Explain how blood flows through the human heart.
- Describe how the respiratory system exchanges carbon dioxide and oxygen in the lungs.
- Explain how the excretory system removes cellular waste from the blood, converts it to urine, and stores it in the bladder before it leaves the body.
- Recognize that the circulatory system transports oxygen and nutrients to cells while removing carbon dioxide and other wastes.
- Put the steps of digestion in the correct order and describe the function of the structures that are part of the digestive process.
- Describe the functions of the immune system.
- Describe the reproductive system of some animals.

PREPARE

Approximate lesson time is 60 minutes.

Materials

For the Student

Come Learn with Me: How Bodies Work: Animal Physiology by Bridget Anderson

📖 Question Review Table

TEACH
Activity 1: Animal Physiology Unit Review (Online)
Instructions

Have your student leaf through the book before beginning the review. Ask her to describe what is being shown in some of the pictures.

ASSESS

Unit Assessment: Animal Physiology (Online)

Students will complete an offline Unit Assessment. Print the assessment and have students complete it on their own. Use the answer key to score the assessment, and then enter the results online. The attached answer key is the most current and may not coincide with previously printed guides.

TEACH
Activity 2. Optional: Unit Assessment Review Table (Online)

Name: _____   Date: _____

Unit Assessment Answer Key

Animal Physiology

Circle the correct answer for questions 1 to 3.

TRUE or FALSE: All body systems help maintain the constant internal environment of the body.

True

Organisms reproduce by two main methods. One is division, where the animal divides and creates an exact copy of itself. What is the other main method of reproduction?

The correct answer is B. fusion.

Which of the following are functions of the immune system? Select the **three** correct answers.

The correct answers are A. Bones produce extra white blood cells to increase its defense against germs, C. Cell membrane keeps germs from entering the cell, and D. Lymphocytes create antibodies that attach to the germ.

Read each question and write your answer below.

Describe how the respiratory system exchanges carbon dioxide and oxygen in the lungs. Include the words *carbon dioxide*, *lungs*, *trachea* and *bronchi* in your answer.

Answers will vary but should include this: Oxygen enters the mouth and nose, and travels down the trachea. The oxygen moves into one of two bronchi that deliver the oxygen to each lung. The diaphragm helps the lungs expand and fill with oxygen. The bronchi branch off into alveoli which lead directly into the bloodstream. At the alveoli, the red blood cells drop off the carbon dioxide and pick up the oxygen from the inhaled air to circulate to body tissues. The carbon dioxide travels back out through the bronchi, trachea and finally, through the nose and mouth.

Explain how blood flows through the human heart. Be sure to include the words *lung*, *valve*, *atrium* and *blood* in your answer.

Answers will vary but should include this: Blood enters the heart through the right atrium. It flows into the right ventricle and is pumped into the lungs. Blood takes in oxygen from the lungs enters the left atrium. It flows into the left ventricle and is pumped into the body's arteries to be carried to the body's cells.

How does the human excretory system filter waste from the blood, store it and then get rid of it? Include the words *kidneys*, *urine* and *bladder* in your answer.

Answers will vary but should include this: The blood transports urea, old cells, excess salt, and unwanted water to the kidneys. The waste and the water from the blood are filtered in the kidneys. This is now called urine. Urine flows through ureter tubes and is stored in the bladder. When the bladder gets full, it exits the body through the urethra.

Sequence the following steps of digestion. Label the first step of digestion 1.

6 The remaining food passes into the large intestine. Water is absorbed from the large intestine and the rest of the material is stored as solid waste.

2 Saliva rushes into the mouth and mixes with the broken down food.

5 The broken down food, called chyme, enters the small intestine.

3 The food travels down the esophagus.

4 The muscles of the stomach churn the food and continue to break it down.

1 The teeth in the mouth bite off a piece of food. The teeth continue to break the food into smaller pieces.

Learning Coach Guide
Lesson 9: Semester Review and Assessment

Your student will review concepts and skills learned during the semester and then take the second Semester Assessment.

Lesson Objectives

- Demonstrate mastery of the semester's content.
- Identify the three main parts of atoms as protons, electrons, and neutrons, and that protons have a positive charge, electrons a negative charge, and neutrons have no charge at all.
- Find the number of protons, electrons, and neutrons in an atom using its atomic number (the number of protons) and mass number (the number of protons and neutrons).
- Use the chemical formula of a compound to identify the elements from which it is composed, and determine the number of each type of atom in the compound.
- Identify the major structures of the cell (such as cell membrane, cytoplasm, and nucleus) and describe their functions.
- Describe the process of *photosynthesis* in plants.
- Explain that traits are passed from parents to offspring and are determined by genes, with an individual having two copies of each gene, one from each parent.
- Name the six kingdoms (Archaebacteria, Eubacteria, Protista, Fungi, Planta, and Animalia) and identify organisms from each.
- Explain how blood flows through the human heart.
- Describe the current model of the atom as a positively charged nucleus containing the protons and neutrons surrounded by electrons moving in certain regions within an "electron cloud".
- Identify four ways to increase the rate of some kinds of chemical reactions (increase the temperature, surface area, concentration, and add a catalyst).
- Use the pH scale to determine whether a solution is acidic or basic.
- Describe how reaction rates increase with temperature, surface area, concentration, and in the presence of a catalyst.
- Recognize the major cell organelles (for example, endoplasmic reticulum, ribosomes, Golgi bodies, chloroplasts, chromosomes, mitochondria, and vacuoles) and describe their functions.
- Define *diffusion* as the process by which molecules move from areas of higher concentration to areas of lower concentration.
- Recognize that water moves through membranes by *osmosis*--diffusion of water through a semipermeable membrane.
- Explain that different types of substances move across the cell membrane by means of diffusion, osmosis, and active transport.
- Identify the seven major levels of classification: Kingdom, Phylum, Class, Order, Family, Genus, and Species.
- Identify one organism in Kingdom Archaebacteria.
- Identify one organism in Kingdom Eubacteria.
- Identify two characteristics common to organisms in Kingdom Protista (thrive in wet environments, most are single celled).
- Identify two organisms in Kingdom Fungi (mushroom, lichens, some molds, yeast).
- Identify two plants in Kingdom Planta.

- Identify two organisms in Kingdom Animalia that are vertebrates.
- Identify the parts of the human respiratory system (nose, mouth, trachea, lungs, diaphragm).
- Describe how the respiratory system exchanges carbon dioxide and oxygen in the lungs.
- Recognize that the circulatory system transports oxygen and nutrients to cells while carrying carbon dioxide and other wastes for removal.
- Identify the structures of the heart (atria, ventricles, valves, major veins and arteries).
- Identify the organs of the excretory system and describe their function (lungs, liver, kidneys, and skin).
- Explain how the excretory system removes cellular waste from the blood, converts it to urine, and stores it in the bladder before it leaves the body.

PREPARE

Approximate lesson time is 60 minutes.

Materials
For the Student

- Periodic Table
- Come Learn with Me: How Bodies Work: Animal Physiology by Bridget Anderson
- Come Learn with Me: The Kingdoms of Life: Classification by Bridget Anderson
- pencil (2)

TEACH
Activity 1: Semester Review (Online)
Instructions
Have your student read through the semester review. Reinforce and explain difficult concepts as needed. Revisit any specific lessons that may have been difficult during the semester.

ASSESS
Semester Assessment: Science 5, Semester 2 (Online)
Students will complete an offline Semester assessment. Print the assessment and have students complete it on their own. Use the answer key to score the assessment, and then enter the results online. The attached answer key is the most current and may not coincide with previously printed guides.

TEACH
Activity 2. Optional: ZlugQuest Measurement (Online)

Name: _____   Date: _____

Semester Assessment Answer Key

1. **C – diffusion**

2. **D – active transport**

3. **A – osmosis**

4. **C – photosynthesis**

5. **A – catalyst**

6. **B – surface area**

7. **C - It transports oxygen and nutrients to cells while removing carbon dioxide and other wastes.**

8. **A – halophile bacteria**

9. **C – cyanobacteria**

10. **A – amoeba; D – seaweed**

11. **B – mushroom; D - mold**

12. **A – moss; C – fern**

13. **A – frog; C – worm**

14. __**False**__ Chemicals packed together tightly react more slowly.

15. ___**True**___ Chemical reactions usually take place more quickly at high temperatures.

16. Match each cell part to its function.

    cytoplasm: D. holds all of the cells organelles

    nucleus: C. directs all of the cell activities

    cell membrane: F. controls what goes in and out of the cell

    chloroplasts: A. in plant cells, converts energy from the sun into glucose.

    chromosome: B. contains all of the genetic information in a cell

17. The nucleus of an atom is made of **protons** and **neutrons**.

18. The **pH scale** is used to indicate whether a solution is acidic or basic.

19. Traits passed down from parent to offspring are determined by **genes**.

20. The nucleus of an atom is surrounded by **electrons**.

21. Label the three main parts of an atom. Then describe their charges.

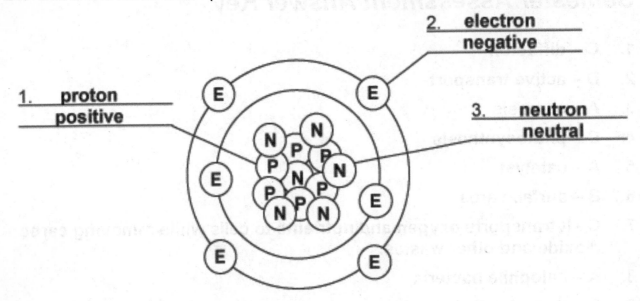

2. **electron**
negative

1. **proton**
positive

3. **neutron**
neutral

22. C$_{12}$H$_{22}$O$_{11}$ **Carbon (12), Hydrogen (22), Oxygen (11)**

23. PbSO$_4$ **Lead (1), Sulfur (1), Oxygen (4)**

Write the compound for the formula described.

24. 1 atom of cobalt ___**CoCl$_2$**___
2 atoms of chlorine

25. 2 atoms of aluminum ___**Al$_2$S$_2$**___
3 atoms of sulfur

26. Name two ways the properties of iron and oxygen are different from the compound iron oxide (rust).

Oxygen is a colorless, odorless gas. Iron is a hard metal. Rust is orange and crumbly.

27. An atom of platinum, Pt, has 78 protons. How many electrons does it contain? **78**

28. Read the list of items and their pH. Classify them according to whether they are an acid, a base, or are neutral.

Soap: 11 **base**

Lemon juice: 2.3 **acid**

Ammonia: 11.5 **base**

Tomatoes: 4.2 **acid**

Stomach acid: 1.4 **acid**

Pure water: 7.0 **neutral**

29. A – Archaebacteria; E – Fungi

30. A – Eubacteria; B – Planta; C – Protista; D – Animalia

31. A – family; B – kingdom; D – class

32. A – phylum; B – species; C – order; D – genus

33. Explain how blood flows through the human heart. Be sure to include the words lungs, atrium, and blood in your answer.

    Answers will vary but should include: Blood enters the heart through the right atrium. It flows into the right ventricle and is pumped into the lungs. Blood full of oxygen from the lungs enters the left atrium. It flows into the left ventricle and is pumped into the body's arteries to be carried to the body's cells.

34. Describe how the respiratory system exchanges carbon dioxide and oxygen in the lungs. Please include the words carbon dioxide, lungs, trachea, and bronchi in your answer.

    Answers will vary but should include: As oxygen enters the mouth and nose, it travels down the trachea. It then moves into one of the two bronchi that then delivers it to each lung. The diaphragm helps the lungs expand and fill with oxygen as this is happening. The bronchi branch off into alveoli and then directly into the bloodstream. The red blood cells drop off the oxygen and pick up the carbon dioxide that needs to leave the body. The carbon dioxide travels back out through the bronchi, trachea, and finally, through the nose and mouth.

35. Put the steps below in order to explain how the excretory system functions.

___3___ Urine flows through ureter tubes and is stored in the bladder.

___2___ Waste and water from the blood are filtered in the kidneys and converted to urine.

___1___ The blood transports urea, old cells, excess salt, and unwanted water to the kidneys.

___4___ When the bladder becomes full, urine exits the body through the urethra.